BEATING STRESS
at work

The **Life Quality Management** series
for anyone balancing the needs of a
healthy lifestyle with the demands of
work. Each book can help you
improve the quality of your life, in
spite of work and its hazards.

Other titles include
Eating Well at Work
Staying Fit at Work
Surviving at Work

Woodham

Published in 1995

Health Education Authority
Hamilton House
Mabledon Place
London WC1H 9TX

© Anne Woodham 1995

ISBN 0 7521 0168 4

A CIP catalogue record for this book is available from the British Library.

Typesetting by Type Generation Ltd.

Printed and bound in Great Britain by
Biddles Ltd, Guildford and King's Lynn

Thank you to the following people for allowing us to reproduce their work on this book:
British Psychological Society, Prof. Cary Cooper, Dr Robert Eliot, David Fontana, Dr Peter Hanson, HEA Look After Your Heart Project, John Nicholson and JC and JD Quick.

Contents

CHAPTER ONE

What is stress?

Never has work seemed so stressful. In fact, it may the biggest source of stress in your life. Even junior office staffers may put in up to 15 hours work a day, and technological developments – mobile telephones, computers, the fax machine – mean that pressure is constant. There is no escape, no time for the body to bounce back and the mind to calm down. No longer does one write a letter to Tokyo and wait a week for the reply; a fax is despatched in the morning and by that afternoon you have a response requesting more information.

A tough economic climate means that employees feel they must be seen to give 200% to their job. Professor Cary Cooper of the Manchester School of Management believes the number of people made ill by work-related stress in the current competitive market is higher than generally held. Mental ill-health and absenteeism is related to the amount of control people feel they have over their work and career development, he says.

Doctors – themselves a deeply stressed profession – report patients queueing with stress-related complaints such as backache, depression and sexual problems. People are told that if they can't keep up the pace, the company will employ someone who can, says a psychiatrist. 'Such people stop taking exercise, start smoking when they had given up, drink more alcohol and coffee. They cannot sleep, lose concentration, become apathetic and finally break down.'

Every working day, an estimated 270,000 people take time off because of stress-related mental illness – a cumulative cost in sick pay, lost production and NHS charges of £7 billion a year.

Employers admit there's a problem. So does the Government. In 1993 Health Secretary Virginia Bottomley launched a major drive to reduce depression, anxiety and other forms of mental illness at work.

And yet only a handful of companies – as few as 13% – have policies or programmes to deal with stress-related illness among employees. Commendable, yes. Sensible, certainly. But where does that leave the vast majority of the working population?

ARE YOU STRESSED?

You may be reading this book because you – or someone close to you – is under the kind of stress that makes it difficult to cope.

Perhaps everything seems on top of you. You're overwhelmed with work – in fact, it would be no surprise to find a pile of documents in your briefcase right now, coming home for a nice dinner and cosy evening with you by the fire. There's so much to do and yet you feel paralysed; you can't think, your brain feels like porridge, and your palms sweat; you're exhausted but you can't sleep; or you fall asleep but wake at four in the morning with your brain running round like a hamster in a wheel. You'd love to get away from it all, but you can't spare the time. Your eyelid twitches, you get tension headaches, and if there's a virus going round the office, then you're bound to go down with it.

You're tense and irritable; even standing in a supermarket queue makes you fidget and rattle the car keys in your pocket, and as for a traffic jam – well, it doesn't bear thinking about. At home, you shout at those near and dear to you, blame your partner personally because the roof has sprung a leak, and have been known, on occasion, to kick the cat.

What is doubly infuriating is that some colleagues under equal pressure seem to actually thrive on it. They come into work looking fresh and enthusiastic; they seem to be always bubbling with ideas; they chat about the things they do outside the office, their family excursions, the tennis club, hiking, sailing; they go to the theatre and they don't fall asleep; they have dinner parties and don't get drunk. Where do they get the energy, you ask.

GOOD AND BAD STRESS

If this is how you feel, it may seem astonishing to learn that stress in itself is not a problem. In fact, it's inescapable, a part of being human. Even standing on our feet against the force of gravity for several hours is a form of stress.

We *need* a certain amount of *pressure* to stimulate us into action: to get up in the morning and go out and find the wherewithal to eat. Positive or *good* stress – sometimes known as *eustress* – is the kickstart that enables us to take pride in a job well done; the little buzz of excitement before a special party or a presentation; the anticipation that we are expected to give our best. It stops life being flat and boring. In fact, people with too much time on their hands and not enough to do suffer from symptoms of stress just as much as those with too little time and too much work.

The causes of stress are known as *stressors*, life events and situations that, when uncontrolled, can pile up and eventually go into overload. They can range from the seriously life-threatening, like a flying bullet or a speeding car, to the benign, like gravity.

Between these two extremes is a vast middle range of stressors, many of them psychological, whose negative impact largely depends on what you *perceive* to be stressful and your capacity to cope with it. Some people, for one reason or another, deal with stressors better than others. Things that you find deeply disturbing wouldn't turn a hair of their heads. Alternatively, they could be deeply anxious over something you take in your stride.

Ultimately, what determines your experience of stress is not the event itself, but the way you think – how much control you feel you have over the problem-causing situations. How you can change your thinking and behaviour so that stress becomes a positive experience is one of the messages of this book.

When you feel in control, then you are more likely to enjoy what you are doing. Even the most seemingly stressful job, from running a multinational corporation to the pizza parlour on the corner, can become not just pleasurable, but invigorating. American psychologist Mihaly Czikszentmihalyi of the University of Chicago describes truly happy workers as being in a state of flow: complete absorption in the activity in hand, a deep sense of exhilaration and clarity, and a feeling that there is nothing one would rather be doing. One's mind and body are in perfect accord, operating at their peak. Musicians feel it when they can no longer say whether they are playing the music or the music is playing them. Time-consciousness disappears: you are so consumed by what you are doing that you are astonished to look up and realise several hours have passed.

Achieving flow involves activity and creativity (although some jobs may seem a darn sight more inspirational than others, Czikszentmihalyi argues that anyone can develop the knack of creating flow). You don't find it slumped in front of the television set, for example. But where to begin? You could start by identifying the obstacles, internal or external, that are causing problems in your life at work and at home. Then you have several options: either to remove them, or learn how to transform them to your advantage.

Imagine, if you can, that you are a bathtub full of water, and imagine all your problems and worries, the things that threaten you, are objects placed in the bath. With the addition of each stress object, the water rises until finally it spills over the top – at which point you lose your temper, have a panic attack, suffer a stroke or some other physical illness, depending on the weak points in your emotional and physical structure. This is why sometimes a tiny incident can provoke an emotional meltdown – your bathtub is nearly full – and at other times – when it's relatively empty – we can handle major emergencies with no apparent effort.

Because we're also different individuals, with different genetic makeups, different temperaments and different growth experiences, our bathtubs will be different sizes. Some people's bath will spill over sooner than others. One of the best ways of handling stress, therefore, is to get to know how big a bathtub you are, and what kind of events will fill it up.

WHAT HAPPENS WHEN YOU'RE STRESSED?

Stress is one of those words that everybody knows the meaning of but no one can define. Psychologist and stress expert Dr Richard Lazarus, of the University of California, describes it as the experience of realising that your situation or environment is taxing your resources and endangering your well-being.

This realisation prompts a primitive reaction, often known as the 'fight-or-flight' response, which is designed to help you cope with a crisis. If you're a caveperson sitting quietly by your campfire thinking of dinner and a sabre-tooth tiger whose idea of a good meal is alarmingly different looms out of the night, your mind and body snaps into defensive mode, ready to either defend yourself or to get the hell out of the place.

All your systems are keyed up, ready to adapt for any kind of action, and so the response is known as the *General Adaptation Syndrome* (GAS), a term coined in the 1950s by Dr Hans Selye, one of the first researchers to make stress a high profile condition.

THIS IS WHAT HAPPENS IN YOUR BODY

- Extra reserves of the stress hormones – adrenaline, noradrenaline and cortisol – flood the system.
- The heart pumps faster. Blood pressure rises to rush blood away from the gut and skin to those parts needing it for emergency action, the muscles of the trunk and limbs.
- Muscles tense.
- The liver releases sugar and fats for fast energy.
- Breathing rate increases to feed more oxygen into the bloodstream for energy.
- Blood clotting agents are on standby, ready to seal injuries.
- Digestion stops to divert power to fighting muscles.
- Saliva dries up and your mouth feels dry.
- Arteries constrict so that less blood is lost if you're wounded
- Perspiration increases; your palms feel sweaty.

And not a sabre-tooth in sight. Just the board of directors, perhaps, awaiting your project presentation.

Dr Selye described three stages of the General Adaptation Syndrome:

1 Alarm reaction – the body's fight-or-flight response
2 Resistance – signs of the alarm reaction diminish and resistance to infectious disease is increased

3 Exhaustion – if there's no escape from the stress situation, or you can't adapt to it, then the alarm reaction returns. It can't be sustained for long, however, before your resources burn out. You eventually collapse, become ill, and even die.

Everyday life is never clear cut; at any given moment we are encountering a combination of internal and external stressors from many sources. But consider how one stress situation can blend into another so that you slip into a downward spiral. You sleep through the alarm, burn the toast, miss the train, arrive at work late to find a meeting has started without you; Martin your pushy deputy scores a point in front of the CEO that makes you look stupid and – even worse – inefficient; the contract bid you were counting on falls through… and so it goes on. Your GAS is going full bore, and your body hasn't had a chance to return to normal.

HOW DO YOU KNOW WHEN YOU'RE STRESSED?

It can happen that people become so accustomed to a certain level of stimulation that they take it for granted. They may not even realise how stressed they really are. James is a commodity broker in the City who works 14-hour days and then spends his weekends shopping compulsively and throwing himself from party to party. 'James doesn't know how to relax'. 'Even when he's watching television, he jiggles his knees all the time. He can't bear going to his parents in the country for the weekend. There's nothing to do except walk through the fields and he gets depressed,' says his partner, Caroline.

James, and others like him, is in an almost permanent state of arousal. The agitated hormones, blood sugars and fats don't get a chance to return to normal and they swill about the body, giving rise to all manner of symptoms – which, if James would only pay attention, are warning him that his coping resources are wearing thin.

Short-term effects of stress are the first key to trouble. After a busy day at work, ask yourself the following questions.

Did I

- enjoy the day?
- have any successes or were they all failures?
- feel alert and on top of events?
- find it hard to grasp what was going on?
- run out of time?
- have difficulty making decisions?
- lose my temper or snap at anyone?
- find myself breathing fast and high in the chest?
- find my neck and shoulders are stiff and aching?

If you answered no to the first three questions, and yes to the rest, look at the other days in the week or month. If your replies are still the same, move on to the following long-term consequences of stress.

Do you suffer from any of the following?

- Aches and pains, especially in the back and chest.
- Heart palpitations.
- Fainting, dizziness, sweating.
- Lack of appetite.
- Craving for food.
- Indigestion, heartburn and stomach aches.
- Nervous twitching and trembling.
- Stammering.
- Nausea.
- Diarrhoea, constipation and frequency in urination.
- Headaches.

● Insomnia.
● Breathlessness without exertion.
● Hyperventilation (or overbreathing).
● Persistent tiredness.
● Frequent coughs, colds and other viral infections.
● Impotence or frigidity.

Do you frequently feel

● depressed?
● irritable?
● lethargic and exhausted?
● unable to cope?
● unable to concentrate?
● that there's never enough time?
● so full of anger that you want to scream?
● anxious for no reason?
● worried over trivial things?
● panicky in routine situations?
● a failure, inefficient and inadequate?
● unable to finish one task before starting another?
● unable to sit still?
● afraid of being alone?
● disinterested in your work, home or other people?
● disinterested in sex?
● dissatisfied with your life without knowing why?
● that you want to cry over 'nothing'?
● that it's hard to make decisions?
● that it's hard to remember anything?
● that you can't talk to people?
● that you want to run away?
● unable to laugh?

Do you

- find it hard to relax?
- bite your nails?
- drink too much alcohol?
- smoke heavily?
- drink too much coffee?
- take tranquillisers or other drugs?
- suffer from phobias and obsessions?
- worry about getting ill?
- give up bothering to wash or take care of your appearance?

These are all physical and emotional symptoms of excessive stress. If you experience any of these frequently – or if you can recall a time when you didn't – then your stress levels are flashing red alert. Read this book, but it would be a good idea to have a chat with your doctor too, as some of these complaints may also be symptoms of physical or mental illness.

IS YOUR PERSONALITY STRESS-PRONE?

Your personality also takes a hand in determining your response to stress (see page 70). In *Understanding Stress* (Which? Books 1992), Dr Chandra Patel refers to 'an intensification of personality traits.... The suspicious person becomes defensive. The careful becomes over-meticulous, the pessimistic lugubrious, the anxious panic-stricken, the inadequate falls to pieces altogether. The irritable becomes explosive, the extrovert becomes slapdash and the introspective loses contact with everyday reality.'

Look around your friends and colleagues and you'll notice how differently everyone responds to life's little challenges. Some individuals fume and fret when they find themselves tenth in the queue at the supermarket; others shrug and take it philosophically. One person may worry themselves to a frazzle, wondering if they'll find a free parking meter when driving into town and what they will do when they can't; another will jump into a car without giving it a moment's thought. American stress experts like Robert S. Eliot refer to these two types as Hot and Cool Reactors. Hot Reactors react to any unfamiliar or ambiguous situations as if they were threatening. Simply anticipating a stressful event will prompt a massive 'fight-or-flight' response, and they feel angry, anxious, fearful, overwhelmed or stretched to the limit much of the time, which puts dreadful strain on their bodies. Cool Reactors, on the other hand, are somehow programmed to take life in as it comes and roll with the punches. The good news is that a majority of Hot Reactors, by following the kind of guidelines listed in this book, can train themselves to stay calm.

What kinds of factors make the difference? In an American survey of executives involved in a difficult company reorganisation, researcher Suzanne Kobasa found that while half the group fell victim to stress-related diseases, the other half – labouring under the same burdens – remained fit and cheerful. She attributed the difference to what she called a 'Hardy Personality,' characterised by the three 'Cs' – commitment, control and challenge.

● Hardy people have a **commitment** to themselves, their job, their family and community and tend to be actively involved in all these spheres.
● They feel in **control** of their lives and believe they influence events.
● They accept that change is part of life and regard it as a **challenge** to explore and experiment.

Stress has been linked to specific illnesses, and even certain kinds of stress to certain complaints. Now it seems possible that particular personality traits could channel stress into corresponding vulnerable parts of the body.

Although family upbringing and individual experiences are responsible for most of our attitudes and opinions, certain basic temperament traits are thought to be inherited. Whether you are optimistic or pessimistic for instance; neat and organised, or spontaneous and chaotic; introverted (you like to relax with a good book in a solitary hammock) or extroverted (you re-energise by throwing a party with bright lights and lots of noise.) Dr Sanford Cohen, of the Stress and Clinical Biobehavioural Medicine Centre, University of Miami, believes that our genes could influence the way in which stress is manifested. One family may be susceptible to gastrointestinal reactions, he says; another to high blood pressure or headaches.

Do you yearn to go bungee-jumping or parachuting? You could be what's called a 'Type T' personality. Thrill-seekers and risk-takers are high-scoring extraverts who are extraordinarily stress-resilient. They seek challenges that others would run a mile to avoid. Experts, such as Professor Hans Eysenck of the Institute of Psychiatry, believe that, due to the way extroverts' brains are wired up, they may be less sensitive to stimulation than introverts.

Chronic, insidious stress such as loneliness, to which introverts and pessimists can be most prone, is thought to target the immune system, the body's defences against disease, leaving you vulnerable to colds and other passing viruses and bacteria.

Hyper-organised control freaks whose defence systems are over-stretched by activity on every front (the guilt-driven working mother, for example, who hurtles home from the office to whip up supper, chivvy the children to piano practice and plan the weekend dinner party) are also more likely to fall victim to colds and other viral infections than laid-back people who set aside non-essential chores while they relax (the parent who leaves plates unwashed to play with the kids).

Anger increases the production of hormones such as

adrenaline and noradrenaline. Not only does this reduce the body's ability to fight disease but can lead to raised blood pressure and heart attacks. Excess stress hormones and fats stoke up cholesterol and clog blood vessels.

In the 1960s, researchers suggested that workaholics with explosive tempers were more prone to heart disease. By the 1970s this impatient, aggressive executive was defined as the Type A personality, and said to be at high risk of a heart attack. Type A has become part of popular mythology, but according to Dr Redford Williams, a behavioural medicine researcher at Duke University, USA, it's not the *enthusiastic* go-getters who are in danger. The lethal element in Type A behaviour is **hostility**.

Feeling hostile is a mixture of cynicism, self-involvement, mistrust and anger. A hostile person believes everyone is out to get them. A queue in the post office is a personal affront. Their boss will do them down (they think), their friends lie, their partners cheat. Such self-obsession is reflected in their speech. People who make heavy use of 'I' and 'my' are twice as likely to suffer heart attacks as more self-effacing souls.

In a recent British study of more than 10,000 civil servants, those with the highest levels of the blood-clotting agent fibrinogen, associated with heart disease, were also the most hostile. These weren't the high-flyers, as it turned out, but those lowest in the pecking order – the most overworked and least in control of their working lives.

Because of their aggressive, distrusting behaviour, hostile people also tend to become isolated. Other people don't want to be around them. American researchers have shown that the more social contacts you have, the better your health is likely to be. Having someone with whom to share worries seems to reduce the biological impact of stress. Even owning a pet can lessen the risk of heart disease.

ARE YOU A HOSTILE TYPE A?

The higher your score in the following questionnaire, the less control you have of your life, the higher your hostility is likely to be, the more stressful your responses, and the greater the risk to your health.

Circle the number that best describes your behaviour over the last 10 years.

	Describe me not at all				Describes me very well		
Being hard driving and ambitious	1	2	3	4	5	6	7
Always rushed	1	2	3	4	5	6	7
Being forceful or dominating	1	2	3	4	5	6	7
Having a strong need to excel in most things	1	2	3	4	5	6	7
Anticipating what others are going to say, finishing their sentences for them	1	2	3	4	5	6	7
Never late	1	2	3	4	5	6	7
Liking and looking for leadership roles	1	2	3	4	5	6	7
Very competitive	1	2	3	4	5	6	7
Trying to do too many things at once, thinking about what to do next	1	2	3	4	5	6	7
Fast eater, walker, etc	1	2	3	4	5	6	7
'Bottling things up' when angry or annoyed	1	2	3	4	5	6	7
Few interests outside work	1	2	3	4	5	6	7
Having difficulty finding time to relax	1	2	3	4	5	6	7

If there is time to relax, it is			
difficult to relax	1 2 3 4	5 6 7	

Over the last few years when
  I have left work, I have often felt:

a) uncertain and dissatisfied with		
how well I was doing	1 2 3 4	5 6 7
b) stretched to the limit of my		
capacity	1 2 3 4	5 6 7
c) that work stays with me		
regularly after hours	1 2 3 4	5 6 7

(Framingham Study, Haynes 1980)

Anxiety is another common stress symptom, especially among those who tend to what psychologists call neuroticism. Neuroticism has had a bad press, associated with hysterics and bizarre obsessions, but it's perfectly possible to have neurotic elements in your personality and still be an effective, functioning human being. You may worry a lot however, especially about minor things, and when under severe strain can slide towards depression, phobias and compulsive behaviour such as checking all electrical appliances are switched off five times over before leaving the house. Anxiety affects the gastrointestinal system, and may contribute to the development of such complaints as ulcers, colitis and irritable bowel syndrome.

STRESS-RELATED DISEASES

Remember that although some people are thought to be more susceptible to certain stress-related complaints than others, this is only a tendency. There is no reason why an extrovert, for example, will not develop a peptic ulcer, nor a meek and gentle soul keel over with a stroke.

Many diseases, from 'flu to arthritis, are associated with the reactions that stress causes in the body and mind, but the links are clearer in some than others. Stress may be a major factor in precipitating the disease, or it may simply exacerbate an existing condition. Common illnesses affecting both men and women that may be stress-related include the following.

Allergy. This is an abnormal sensitivity to particular foods, plants, animals or insect bites. Results include migraine, eczema, rashes, wheezing, sneezing, fatigue, nausea and diarrhoea. The body's immune system has mistaken harmless substances, such as pollen, dust or wheat, for dangerous invaders and gone into overdrive. Breathing or touching even tiny amounts of these substances, known as *allergens*, will release protein substances called *antibodies* and the reaction between the two triggers more chemicals called *histamines*, which are the real culprits in the allergic reaction.

Animal hair, feathers, plants, soap and cosmetics are common allergens; so are certain foods – milk, cheese, flour, shellfish, nuts, chocolate and artificial colourings. People can rub along quite happily with these and then suddenly find – usually when they're under strain of various kinds and their coping mechanisms are at full stretch – that they're itching or wheezing or feeling that a ton of old clothes has been dumped on them.

Asthma can have a strong allergic component in some people. The bronchial tubes secrete excess mucus, which inflames and narrows the tubes and makes it harder for air to reach the lungs. Breathing is difficult, in itself a source of further panic.

Baldness. Periods of stress have been related to *alopecia areata*, where hair falls out in handfuls, leaving unsightly and motheaten bald patches. It can affect the scalp (women sufferers frequently resort to wigs) and eyebrow and body hair. The good news is that the hair usually grows back.

Cancer. There is increasing evidence that the way you cope with stress can contribute to the development of some cancers. It's a controversial issue – not least because of the onus that is thrown back on the individual: is your disease your 'fault'? – but a number of scientific studies highlight a connection between emotions, hormones and physical responses. The biological pathways linking mind and body have yet to be discovered, although many scientists suspect that chemical messengers called neurotransmitters are implicated in suppressing immune responses which normally protect against cancer cells.

Dr Stephen Greer of the Royal Marsden Hospital established that patients with a defeatist response to breast cancer had less chance of recovery than those with a fighting spirit. In the US, psychologist Dr Lydia Temoshok investigated links between stress and coping in patients with malignant skin cancer. She found that hardline stoics who refused to admit to fear or anger had the most rapidly advancing cancers. But the mind's responses are complicated. Other researchers report that a certain kind of denial ('okay, I've got cancer, but I'm not going to let it get in the way of my life') is effective in combating the disease.

Another American psychiatrist, Dr David Spiegel at the University of California, has shown that when women with advanced breast cancer were encouraged to face the concept of death and formed emotional bonds in a support group, they survived twice as long as others.

Depression (see also page 113). Most of us feel low when things are tough, but in some people – when stress is combined with other factors such as personality, environment, genes and upbringing – full-blown depression can result. More women than men are depressed, but this probably has much to do with the struggle to reconcile a job and family, the obligation to do too much or the ennui of not doing enough. When it comes to manic depression, a condition in which moods swing violently from elation to suicidal despair, men are as susceptible as women.

A number of the symptoms of depression also relate to stress itself, which highlights the involvement of one with the other. However, if at least four of the following apply to you and have done so for two weeks or more despite all efforts to shake them off, make an appointment to see your GP.

● A loss of interest and enjoyment in life.
● A lack of drive and motivation, that makes even simple tasks and decisions difficult or impossible.
● Utter fatigue.
● Agitation and restlessness.
● Loss or gain in appetite, with loss or gain in weight.
● Sleeplessness or excessive sleeping.
● Loss of outward affection; going off sex.
● Loss of self-confidence; avoiding meeting people.
● Irritability.
● Feeling useless, inadequate, bad, helpless and hopeless.
● Feeling worse at a particular time of the day, usually mornings.
● Thoughts of suicide – a certain sign that help is needed.

Diabetes. The failure of the pancreas to produce the hormone insulin which helps convert blood sugar to energy is known as *diabetes mellitus*. Although physical or emotional stress can bring latent diabetes into the open, it is unlikely to induce it in a healthy individual.

Headaches. Stress is a notorious trigger of tension and migraine headaches. Muscles taut from long hours of concentration, boardroom confrontation or from sitting in an awkward position – hunched behind the driving wheel, or in front of a word processor – will often provoke a tension headache.

A migraine is a specific type of headache due to spasms and relaxations of blood vessels covering the brain. The attack usually starts with the 'aura' (flares or zigzag patterns) and the headache follows, accompanied by nausea, vomiting and sensitivity to light.

Both can be treated with painkillers of varying strengths, but there are several techniques that may bring relief without drugs, especially for tension headaches.

High blood pressure (Hypertension). Blood pressure rises in response to a stressful situation, and goes up and down numerous times a day whenever we exercise or our emotions are aroused. In most cases it returns to normal once the excitement is over. Sometimes, if the rise is severe or prolonged, there are changes in the arteries which mean the blood pressure remains high. But when people suffer from hypertension it is not necessarily due to stress – the condition may run in the family or be due to underlying medical conditions. When coupled with narrowed and hardened arteries, exacerbated by smoking and blood fats, it can cause strokes and brain haemorrhages. It makes sense therefore for people with high blood pressure to learn to handle excessive stress. Relaxation and meditation techniques have been shown to reduce blood pressure (see page 90).

Heart disease. When the blood supply to the heart is reduced because the coronary arteries are clogged up with fatty deposits, you can suffer from angina, an acute pain across the chest and sometimes in the neck, jaw or arm. Stressful emotions like anxiety, fear and hostility, which release stress hormones into the bloodstream and put the heart on overdrive, can prompt an angina attack. Add a blocked artery, and you have a heart attack. For some people, drugs such as beta-blockers may help, as may relaxation, yoga, a low fat diet, moderate activity and supportive relationships.

STRESSBREAKERS

- *Progressive relaxation* (see page 90)

- *Acupressure.* In traditional Chinese medicine, stimulating certain points on the body is said to restore the flow of healing life energy, known as qi. Begin on your face, just above the cheekbone and beside the eyes, then slowly work your way down the line of the jaw. Press with the ball of the thumb or tips of the fingers, increasing the pressure gradually to about 5 grams (practise on the kitchen scales), and make tiny circular movements in a clockwise direction. Release slowly and gently after 20 seconds. Wait for ten seconds and then repeat up to five times. Massage the bridge of your nose between your thumb and first finger. Repeat this pressure, using both hands, on the back of the neck, just below the hairline.

- *Yoga breathing* (pranayama). The following is known as alternate nostril breathing or sun and moon breath. Sit upright, close your right nostril with the thumb of one hand and inhale through the left nostril to the count of two. With the third (or ring) finger of the same hand, close the left nostril and hold your breath to the count of eight. Release your thumb and exhale through the right nostril to the count of four. Then inhale right to two, hold for eight and exhale left for four. Repeat ten times. With practise, increase the ratio of breathing in, holding and breathing out to 4:16:8.

- *Physical activity.* Take a break and go for a walk or run; limber up with some exercises.

Irritable Bowel Syndrome. Frequent stomach pains and cramps, bloating, diarrhoea, constipation and, less often, heartburn may be signs of irritable bowel syndrome (IBS). Although there is no known cause or cure, it's thought that stress could make the problem worse by sending the colon into spasm, especially if there is insufficient bulk working its way through the bowel. In general, IBS sufferers seem more susceptible to stress. Drugs are sometimes prescribed, but relaxation exercises, avoiding high fat foods and caffeine and adding fibre to the diet can soothe the symptoms.

Peptic ulcers. Stress itself may not cause ulcers, which some experts now believe are due to a type of bacteria, but it can worsen the situation by increasing gastric acid in the stomach. An ulcer occurs when there is a gap in the mucous lining the stomach and the acid attacks the stomach wall.

Skin diseases. Skin diseases such as eczema, urticaria (hives), acne and psoriasis are all aggravated by stress. The unpleasantness and embarrassment of the complaints can add to the anxiety. Eczema is associated with hay fever and asthma (see ***Allergy***) and typically gets worse at times of tension. Harry, for instance, had six months of sheer hell, setting up a new high-risk department in a climate of backstabbing and criticism.'My hands were practically raw with eczema. Now that things have calmed down and it's going well, the rash is beginning to subside.'

CHAPTER TWO

What causes stress?

LIFE EVENTS

Apart from the immediately lethal, such as a runaway bus or an attacker with a knife, many of the stress situations that modern men and women encounter are what are known as 'life events'. These inevitably involve change of one kind or another – and change, even when it appears happy, as in marriage, can mean breaking familiar routines and adjusting to new ones, and thus may become a source of stress.

Two American researchers in the 1960s, Dr Thomas Holmes and Dr Richard Rahe, developed a 'Social Readjustment Rating Scale' – more commonly known as 'the Stress Chart' – which has been used to assess the degree of trauma under which you may be labouring. Points on a scale of 1 to 100 were allotted to major life events such as bereavement, marriage, divorce and moving house, and, by adding up which of these you had experienced in the last 12 months, you could, in theory, work out your chances of developing a stress-related illness.

Such scores can seem rather arbitrary. Parents might give a hollow laugh to learn that childbirth rated only 39 points, and the economic ramifications of divorce for a working mother could differ somewhat from those of a childless professional couple.

Nevertheless, many people are unaware that they are experiencing excessive stress. The following test from the HEA 'Look After Your Heart; Look After Yourself' project, with some questions adapted from the Holmes and Rahe 'Life Change Rating

Scale', University of Washington Medical School 1967, can help you determine your level of stress. Answer the questions in terms of the last 12 months; count the number of points for each 'yes' answer.

Have you lived or worked in a noisy area?	**3**
Have you changed your living conditions or moved?	**3**
Have you had trouble with in-laws?	**3**
Have you taken out a large loan or mortgage?	**3**
Have you tended to fall behind with the things you should do	**3**
Have you found it difficult to concentrate at times?	**3**
Have you frequently had trouble going to sleep?	**3**
Have you found you tend to eat, drink or smoke more than you really should?	**3**
Have you watched three or more hours of television daily for weeks at a time?	**·3**
Have you or your spouse changed jobs or work responsibilities?	**4**
Have you been dissatisfied or unhappy with your work or felt excessive work responsibility?	**4**
Has a close friend died?	**4**
Have you been dissatisfied with your sex life?	**4**
Have you been pregnant?	**4**
Have you had an addition to the family?	**4**

Have you worried about making ends meet?	4
Has one of the family had bad health?	4
Have you taken tranquillisers from time to time?	4
Have you frequently found yourself becoming easily irritated when things don't go well?	4
Have you often experienced bungled human relations – even with those you love most	4
Have you found that you're often impatient or edgy with your children or other family members?	4
Have you tended to feel restless or nervous a lot of the time?	4
Have you had frequent headaches or digestive upsets?	5
Have you experienced anxiety or worry for days at a time?	5
Have you often been so preoccupied that you have forgotten where you've put things (such as keys) or forgotten whether you've turned off appliances on leaving home or office?	5
Have you been married or reconciled with your spouse?	5
Have you had a serious accident, illness or surgery?	5
Has anyone in your immediate family died?	6
Have you divorced or separated?	7

Scoring. Fill in total points for 'yes' answers. 1–10 points: You're in great shape. Congratulations! 11–20 points: You obviously have some stress, but seem to be coping with it. Watch out for increases in stressful situations. 21–35 points: You are entering the danger zone. You should try to take the pressure off yourself. Over 36 points: You are under an excessive amount of stress. We would advise you to consult your doctor for a medical check-up and avoid taking on additional pressures.

EVERYDAY STRESSES

Underlying life-changing events are the numerous and constant stress triggers that are part of everyday living: traffic hold-ups, cancelled trains, busy telephone lines, deadlines, confrontations, exasperations, and resentments. Not so traumatic in themselves, but added together they can make a formidable load.

Our jobs, occupying so much of our day, will inevitably contribute to the worries and aggravations that are filling up our stress bathtub. But – and this is important – they are also an integral part of our identity and a source of great satisfaction, camaraderie, challenge and pleasure. Ask people what they are, not just what they do, and they will still reply 'a lawyer,' 'a department store buyer,' 'a carpenter'. When you enjoy your job and take pride in it, pressure is not seen as stress: it boosts self-esteem and enhances your health.

The effects of stress at work not only take their toll on the individual concerned, but knock on to his or her colleagues and even throughout the company. 'My boss was always criticising and picking fault. It didn't matter if it was a mega project or absolute trivia. Praise or gratitude just weren't in his vocabulary. Of course, it was the deepest part of the recession and his job was on the line. You could tell he was under strain, but it still meant we took the flak, and it certainly didn't help us do our jobs any better,' says Gerry, a junior advertising account executive.

Not only does performance suffer, but people can't concentrate, too much energy is squandered on unproductive work, they become irrational and take wrong and ill-considered decisions. 'I'd find myself looking from one fabric sample to another. Maybe it should be that one. Or would this one be better? Was it too dark? Perhaps it was too floral? I felt completely paralysed, and this dithering wasted hours. Sometimes I'd just shut my eyes and stab at one in order to get on. No judgement at all,' says Mari, a self-employed interior decorator.

Consider everything that hangs on one's occupation: not only identity and satisfaction, but status, power, income, the mortgage, children's education, the car, social contacts, a holiday, nice clothes – the list becomes endless. The threat of losing any of this is inevitably seen as stressful.

But bear in mind that everyone responds differently, according to their individual make-up. What might be too much responsibility for one person will be insufficiently challenging for another. The computer programmer's job that an exuberant extrovert finds boring could be meat and drink to a quieter, introverted personality who likes being left alone. Professor Cary Cooper's Work Stress Questionnaire below allows you to identify the areas that might be particularly difficult for you.

What part of your job is most stressful?

Circle the number that best reflects the degree to which the statement is a source of stress for you at work

	No stress at all		Stress	A great deal of stress		
work overload	0	1	2	3	4	5
work underload	0	1	2	3	4	5
time pressure and deadlines	0	1	2	3	4	5
the amount of travel required by my work	0	1	2	3	4	5
long working hours	0	1	2	3	4	5
taking my work home	0	1	2	3	4	5
lack of power and influence	0	1	2	3	4	5
attending meetings	0	1	2	3	4	5
my beliefs conflicting with those of the organisation	0	1	2	3	4	5
keeping up with new technology	0	1	2	3	4	5
threat of job loss	0	1	2	3	4	5
competition for promotion	0	1	2	3	4	5
having to move with my job in order to advance my career	0	1	2	3	4	5

doing a job beyond my level of competence	0	1	2	3	4	5
doing a job below my level of competence	0	1	2	3	4	5
inadequately trained subordinates	0	1	2	3	4	5
interpersonal relations	0	1	2	3	4	5
hiring and firing personnel	0	1	2	3	4	5
unsympathetic boss	0	1	2	3	4	5
incompetent boss	0	1	2	3	4	5
performance-related compensation	0	1	2	3	4	5
unrealistic objectives	0	1	2	3	4	5
dealing with conservation groups	0	1	2	3	4	5
dealing with shareholders	0	1	2	3	4	5
dealing with unions	0	1	2	3	4	5
my partner's attitude towards my career	0	1	2	3	4	5
demands of work on my relationship with my family	0	1	2	3	4	5
demands of work on private and social life	0	1	2	3	4	5
my relationship with my colleagues	0	1	2	3	4	5

my relationship with my subordinates	0	1	2	3	4	5
making mistakes	0	1	2	3	4	5
feeling undervalued	0	1	2	3	4	5
promotion prospects	0	1	2	3	4	5
rates of pay	0	1	2	3	4	5
managing people	0	1	2	3	4	5
office politics	0	1	2	3	4	5
lack of consultation and communication in my organisation	0	1	2	3	4	5

Scoring. The maximum score is 185, but a total of over 100 indicates that the overall stress in your working life could do with some reassessment.

Professor Cooper and his researchers found that there are five major categories of work stress:

1 Factors intrinsic to the job
2 Role in the organisation
3 Relationships at work
4 Career development
5 Organisational structure and climate.

CHAPTER THREE

You and your job

IS YOUR JOB HIGH-STRESS?

Certain occupations are intrinsically more stressful than others. A research assistant in a library is not likely to encounter the same demands on his or her decision-making skills, readiness to take responsibility or calmness under pressure as an airline pilot, casualty doctor or managing director. The day of a teacher in a rural primary school will be somewhat different from that of one teaching in a tough, inner-city secondary school. (On the other hand, factors such as office intrigue or a bad relationship with your boss will add a negative spin to almost any post.)

Examples of high-stress jobs

- policeman/woman (physical danger and unpopularity in some quarters)
- miner or machine operator (unpleasant working conditions)
- doctor (long hours and high responsibility contribute to high rates of alcoholism, drug abuse, depression, suicide and divorce)
- nurse (underpaid and overworked)
- journalist (constant deadlines and competition)
- actor (uncertainty of work and need to keep a high profile)
- traffic warden (nobody likes you)
- dentist (do patients come in smiling?)
- teacher (heavy work load, lack of control, possible lack of status, disruptive and disinterested pupils)
- office manager (you're the filling in the sandwich between

senior management and suspicious junior staff)
● secretary (low status and little control of your work)
● foreman (dealing with management on one hand and unions on the other; blue collar workers run a higher risk of coronaries and heart disease from stress than executives)
● waitress or waiter (low status, people order you about and long hours on your feet)

Examples of low-stress jobs
● museum curator
● gardener
● librarian
● farm labourer
● craftsman
● computer programmer

If you are an extrovert who craves action and excitement, however, then a low-stress job could become high-stress; boredom from lack of stimulation may drive you to distraction.

ARE YOU IN THE RIGHT JOB FOR YOUR PERSONALITY?

Take air traffic control. This is a job for calm, methodical personalities – not for those of an excitable and spontaneous temperament. If your occupation is out of kilter with your personality and you feel like a square peg in a round hole, you are also likely to feel stressed.

An estate agent who tends to be passive and lacking in self-confidence, for example, won't sell too many houses. His lack of success will demoralise and distress him. If there are elements of your job that make you uncomfortable and that you find difficult to deal with, consider whether you are really suited to such an occupation. You may not necessarily have to abandon it, but you could explore ways of compensating for troublesome aspects.

'I'd been a staff writer on a Canadian newspaper, and when I came to London looking for a job, I followed the footsteps of many another journalist and joined a public relations company. A week in the place and I knew I'd made a mistake. I thought all the accounts were ghastly and I simply couldn't face the prospect of cold-calling newspaper and magazine editors and pretending I had some wonderful story. Fortunately I landed a job as an assistant editor with the BBC and with one bound I was free,' says Andrew, an amiable but rather earnest young man.

HOW HEALTHY ARE YOUR WORKING CONDITIONS?

Environment

Some workplaces should be labelled 'mad, bad and dangerous to work in.' Factories can be noisy, hot and smelly, and the constant effort of adapting to the din wears down workers' coping mechanisms and affects their relationships with each other. But even plush offices have their own insidious forms of environmental strain that affect physical and mental health. If any of the following are a problem, try and discuss possible improvements with the management.

Air conditioning systems. When carbon monoxide, form-aldehyde and other toxic gases, air ions, viruses and bacteria are recirculated endlessly through the air conditioning system, they can cause sore eyes, allergies, dry skin, headaches and respiratory infections. Over-enthusiastic **central heating** dries moisture from the air and debilitates the brain. Ideal working temperature is 20°C (68° F). Too much either side of this and energy levels drop.

STRESSBREAKER

Open windows for natural ventilation as much as possible, outside noise and traffic pollution permitting.

Air ions. These positively and negatively charged particles affect brain hormones. Fresh air abounds in negative ions which keep you calm and clear-headed; positive ions, found in heavy traffic and stuffy air-conditioned offices, can make you irritable and depressed. If your office is 'sick', make a point of getting outside – away from traffic, needless to say – at lunchtime and after work.

STRESSBREAKER

Invest in an ioniser, an inexpensive electrical appliance that converts positive ions to negative.

Noise. A high level of background noise is very wearing. In offices, telephones, chattering voices, and humming machinery such as computers and photocopiers distract concentration. Hospital wards, schools and other institutions also have a high level of background noise.

STRESSBREAKER

Adjust telephone bells to a lower level

Position photocopiers away from work areas

VDUs. Word processors and computers are blamed for just about everything: eyestrain, sore necks and backs, insomnia, headaches, irritability, tension, fatigue, repetitive strain injury and radiation. Much of this can be countered if your workstation and chair are correctly positioned, and you do not sit in front of the VDU for too long at a time. As in so many areas, job satisfaction counters many of these stressful symptoms. Bored and unmotivated workers succumb easily to stress symptoms.

STRESSBREAKER

Stand up and stretch every 20 minutes, and every hour or so get up and walk around.

Space. Work performance is affected by the way in which an office is designed. Open plan offices, with their lack of privacy, prove unpopular – humans are territorial animals – but on the other hand, when staff need frequent liaison, too much compartmentalisation makes communication difficult, demoralising relationships and confusing roles.

STRESSBREAKER

Personalise your office or desk space with plants, fresh flowers, pictures, cards, posters. US research has shown these touches improve productivity.

Light. The lighting needs to fit the job. Not enough, for close detailed work, and you'll suffer eyestrain. Too much artificially bright and garish light, as in hospitals, can lead to feelings of claustrophobia and dehumanisation.

STRESSBREAKER

Investigate weaker or tinted bulbs or full spectrum lighting.

Working hours

Shift work. Humans increasingly work staggered hours to match modern technology's 24-hour day. Air traffic controllers, night news editors, nurses and police officers are just some of the millions of people likely to be working at 2am. Not only sleep patterns and family life are affected; so are blood temperature, metabolic rate, blood sugar levels, the immune system (more colds and viruses sneak in), mental efficiency (more accidents) and work motivation.

Long hours. The recent death of a junior hospital doctor, who averaged nearly 80 hours work a week and routinely missed sleep for 24 to 36 hours, focussed attention (yet again) on the effects on health of such punishing hours. Yet it's not unusual for executives to arrive grey-faced for a 7am meeting after working all night – and be admired for their zeal. They should take a few leaves from the book of safety-conscious airlines who meticulously monitor pilots' duty rosters. Working weeks that regularly exceed 40 hours are increasingly seen (by psychologists and enlightened companies) as counter-productive and a waste of time: tired people are neither efficient nor innovative.

STRESSBREAKERS

- Try to sleep at the same time every day. If you feel tired, take a nap before starting a night shift.
- Make the room as dark as possible when sleeping during the day, or use an eye mask to cut out light.
- Exercise as much as possible during a night shift: walk up stairs rather than take the lift; place the phone where you'll have to get up to answer it.

Does travel get you down?

Commuting. People stuck in a traffic jam don't have much option over the fight-or-flight response to stress. Flight is usually out of the question, so they're left with fight. Adrenaline surges, tempers flare, drivers cut in on each other and shout abuse. Lorna, a well-mannered PA, is shocked at herself. 'I made a two-finger gesture at another driver this morning. This man was tooting his horn in the most ridiculous way, and I just saw red. I don't know what came over me.'

Travelling by road shows no signs of improving. As the population increases and more people buy second and third cars, main roads are clogged with bottlenecks and side roads congested with parked cars. Driving five miles across London can take over an hour in rush-hour traffic.

STRESSBREAKERS

● If your journey usually takes 45 minutes, allow yourself an hour. That way unexpected snarl-ups won't agitate you.

● Use a cassette recorder to note down ideas, plan speeches, dictate letters as you wait.

● Choose soothing music on your car stereo or radio.

● Study by audiotape. Brush up your French, or listen to a novel.

● Listen to comedy tapes and laugh.

● Practise relaxation skills (see page 90) while stuck in a traffic jam (not while driving!).

● Invest in a car phone (if you don't already have one) so that you can keep up with business calls. Lap-top computers, modems and fax machines can now be used in cars – but not while driving!

Rail is often little better for stress levels. City and surburban trains are overcrowded, and at the mercy of security alerts and delays; cancellations and signal failures plague regional lines. Many workers cope by withdrawing into a private world with their portable stereos.

Michael, an architect, confesses that it was the horror of commuting daily on the Undergound in rush-hour that finally drove him to transfer his office to a suburban site only a mile from his home. 'The stress of being crammed in a tunnel with so many people, standing knee to groin, was really getting to me. I was coming home later and later, putting off the journey, and spending a fortune on taxis. Now I'm at work in minutes by car, or I can walk it in a quarter of an hour.'

Not all train travel is a strain. People with long inter-city commutes find them less tiring than those in suburban cattle trucks because they can sit down and read.

Jet lag. Despite the proliferation of fax machines, e-mail and telephones, there's often no alternative but to board a plane and meet face to face, or see a factory or project for yourself. Plane travel is wonderful but can take a terrible toll on the mind and body. Poor concentration, slow reflexes, irritability and upset digestion are just some of the effects of jet lag. Our internal clocks take days to adjust to a new rhythm; sleeping when we should be awake, bright-eyed and bushy-tailed when we should be asleep. Executives are expected to step off a night flight from New York or Tokyo and take vital decisions at a top-level meeting. Unfair perhaps, but when one heavily jet-lagged businessman dozed off in the boardroom, his card was marked for redundancy. And worrying about your performance when you're red-eyed and sleep-hungry is another source of stress.

STRESSBREAKERS

- Fly business class if you or your company can afford it. Wider seats and more leg room enable you to stretch your limbs and rest. Your arrival in a better condition will compensate for the extra cost. Some companies actually insist that senior executives fly first class if the journey crosses multiple time zones and they have to hit the ground running.

- Adopt your destination time as soon as you arrive. Even if it's early in the morning, keep yourself awake until the evening.

- Choose eastward flights as early as possible to arrive in daylight. Choose westward flights to arrive in darkness.

- Use light and dark to help you adjust. Bright sunlight will help convince your internal clock it should be awake in Sydney, even though it's bedtime back in London. An eye mask will help you ignore daylight to sleep in-flight.

- Judicious use of sleeping tablets can help adjust sleep patterns. If taken for brief periods, there's little risk of side effects. Ask your GP about Zolpidem, a new non-addictive, fast-acting sleeping pill that comes from a family of drugs called imidazopyridines.

- A growing number of travellers swear by small doses of melatonin, a naturally occurring hormone secreted by the pineal gland in a daily pattern, signalling the approach of night and prompting sleep. A simple substance that is easy and cheap to manufacture, and therefore an unattractive commercial proposition for expensive development by a pharmaceutical company, it is available by mail order or from specialist shops, such as Revital Health Shop (see Resources for address).

- Eat high-protein meals to keep you awake, a light carbo-hydrate meal several hours before you want to sleep.
- Avoid alcohol and caffeine in flight, and drink plenty of still water to avoid dehydration.
- Exercise as much as you can during the flight. Stroll up and down the aisle, circle your ankles and wrists, raise and lower your shoulders before tilting your head smoothly from left to right. Exercise more freely on arrival, but not too strenuously on the first day.
- Some airlines offer dehydration gels and face sprays. Experienced travellers recommend applying moisturiser frequently in flight and, if worn, removing all makeup after take-off.

New technology

Computers may cut through old paperwork methods like a knife through butter, but they can throw a fair amount of stress about too. A lot of people think that once they've finished school or college, they're finished with learning, and then, lo and behold, there's a computer or word processor winking at you, and the strong message that if you don't get acquainted with it, your career will pass you by.

The older one is, the more intimidating new technology can be. This doesn't apply only to 45-year-old secretaries wrestling with WordPerfect; senior managers struggle to keep up with computer developments that their junior colleagues embrace with infuriating ease. Every parent knows that children these days are born practically wired into the video recorder and the Nintendo.

STRESSBREAKER

Think positive. New technology may seem daunting but hands-on practice soon acclimatises you. Make sure professional back-up is at hand.

Overworked or underworked?

Just as too heavy a workload can lead to anxiety, frustration and exhaustion, too little work also causes stress. This may be due to inactivity – such as that encountered by those doing night security work – or a job that doesn't stretch your abilities. Boring and unstimulating work lowers self-esteem and denies job satisfaction. Both extremes can contribute towards a dependence on nicotine, alcohol or drugs. People in some jobs – airline pilots or firefighters, for example – swing from long periods of doing relatively little to bursts of intense activity. Maintaining maximum alertness and skill in these circumstances can be stressful.

Working from home

The wonders of high-tech communication means that more people can elect to work from home, but a particular kind of personality and a fair degree of motivation is needed. Without the presence of colleagues it's easy to feel out of touch with events and let paranoia creep in. Any rebuffs or setbacks can hit harder without a mate to defuse the hurt. If you're a freelancer working for yourself, there's the additional stress of wondering where the next assignment is coming from.

While advantages include no commuting and closer links with the family, sometimes the office seems ever-present, and the temptation to succumb to workaholism and stay glued at the desk into the evenings and over the weekend can be hard to resist.

On the upside, a recent American survey found that home-based workers were extremely happy, even when working long hours and not making much money.

STRESSBREAKERS

- If space permits, work in a specially set-aside room. You can shut the door and walk away when it's time to relax.
- Establish set times to start and finish work, and stick to them.
- Be firm about non-essential interruptions. Friends and neighbours can regard home-based workers as constantly available.
- Make a point of meeting socially with a colleague or friend in a similar line of business at least once a week.
- If you have difficult phone calls to make, boost morale by inviting a friend in a similar line of business to work at your place while you ring. Arrange to reciprocate.

CHAPTER FOUR

You and the organisation

YES, BUT WHAT DO YOU ACTUALLY *DO*?

Wondering where you fit into an organisation and what is expected of you is stressful. It may be the fault of your superior, who has not made clear what your job involves. Even where there's a job description carefully drafted by the personnel department, it can prove too vague, or your line manager chooses to ignore it. Regular appraisals should provide an opportunity to clarify matters, but it's surprising in how many companies these are allowed to slip, or don't happen at all.

'We were supposed to have appraisals once every six months. My boss would put it off and put it off until Personnel nagged him into it. Then he'd never schedule enough time – we'd have to break off because of an urgent phone call or a meeting – and he'd say well, everything's fine, isn't it. Then I heard that he'd been complaining that I wasn't putting enough effort into following up contacts. He never mentioned that to me as an issue. In fact, when I'd specifically raised the question of contacts, he said it wasn't important. I mean, where do I stand?,' says Nick, a sales representative.

Clare works as a secretary PA to two junior executives who have quite different management styles. One, a woman, leans on her for personal help: picking up dry cleaning, leaving messages with the nanny. The other, a man, suddenly appears at her desk with a pile of 'urgent' work, insisting that it be done within the hour. 'I literally feel torn in two. One moment I'm twiddling my thumbs, the next they're both at me, each demanding priority.'

Senior executives can find themselves adrift, especially after a corporate takeover or management restructuring. 'Every time I asked for a definition of my role, I'd be told it was in the pipeline, they'd have something concrete in a month or two. I took to coming in late and sloping off for long lunch hours, saying I had business appointments, anything so the junior staff wouldn't see me hanging about,' complains Charles, an assistant general manager whose carpet manufacturing company was swallowed up by a multinational.

AND DO YOU *LIKE* IT?

If your job does not agree with your value systems – your beliefs and attitudes – then you can feel uncomfortable and compromised. In the long run your self-esteem could be damaged and your health placed at risk. Examples of this kind of conflict might be an idealistic journalist working for a tabloid newspaper; a nurse who finds that increased administration cuts into time spent caring for patients; an environmentally minded scientist working for a chemical company.

Sometimes loyalties are in conflict. Sales staff report high tension when they are caught between the opposing demands of customers and suppliers.

IS YOUR PERFORMANCE UP TO SCRATCH?

In an increasingly ruthless market, the idea of a cushy job for life has disappeared in a puff of smoke. Performance is all and employees must remain alert. If annual targets are not achieved, bonuses will be docked and the threat of redundancy is ever-present. A system of appraisals, where effectively operated, provides an opportunity for review and assessment, but this is often a cause in itself for anxiety and apprehension.

The growth of consultancies, freelance and contract work means that cohorts of hungry professionals are in cut-throat competition. Standards must be high and deadlines met in order to survive.

WHAT ARE YOU RESPONSIBLE FOR?

Responsibility for people is seen as more stressful than responsibility for things, such as budgets or equipment.

If you're a manager, you're aware that your staff's performance will reflect on you, and therefore that you have an obligation to ensure that they feel secure and well-motivated. On the other hand, especially during the lean years of recession, the right to hire and fire can seem like a poisoned chalice. To make anyone redundant, or to fire someone you have employed, is a distressing task.

Senior managers carry responsibility for the successful running of the company; their decisions dictate expansion or contraction, profits and losses, and ultimately the jobs of employees. At the highest level, chief executives may find the strain of decision-making spread among their advisers but be afflicted with the particular stress of loneliness. The only people who understand their problems are other chief executives and managing directors and they are all too busy to meet each other.

Middle and junior managers suffer from being the filling in the sandwich: with responsibility but no authority, and little or no control over decisions taken by senior managers that will affect their department – a combination known to be associated with heart disease. The various roles they are expected to perform can tear them apart: on one hand representing the interests of their subordinates, and on the other passing on the dictum of their superiors. Where there is union representation and industrial disputes, supervisors can find themselves playing an uncomfortable piggy in the middle, especially if they have been promoted from the ranks and have some empathy with the 'workers.'

If promotion has passed them by (and not *everybody* can squeeze into the directors' boardroom) middle managers may feel trapped, embittered and at risk. Should redundancy be in the air, who goes first? The older man or woman, loyal but limited, set in the habits of a lifetime? Or the young turk snapping at his heels?

ARE YOU MANAGING AS WELL AS YOU SHOULD?

All managers experience pressure in their jobs, but there are warning signals when challenge turns to stress. Occupational psychologist John Nicholson devised the following quiz (*How Do You Manage?* BBC Books 1992)

	Yes	No
1 Far too much to do		
2 Not enough influence over what needs to be done		
3 The people I manage are too demanding		
4 Not enough support from above		
5 Too many new ideas to cope with		
6 People don't back me up		
7 My job pulls me in too many different directions at once		
8 They're always moving the goalposts		
9 Having to deal with 'difficult' situations		
10 Personality clashes with colleagues		

Scoring. Allow yourself a point for every 'Yes' ticked. The higher your score, the more sources of pressure in your job. If you've scored more than four, take a hard look at how you handle things. Which pressure points are identified? Should you be looking for more control over the way you operate, or ask people for more support? Do you need to rethink how you organise your time? (See page 106.)

CLIMBING THE LADDER OF SUCCESS

Here is a fact of life: there are very few people at the very top. Not all of us will achieve the dreams with which we began our careers. Ambition, competitiveness, envy, boredom, pride, vanity, greed, revenge, excitement, altruism, determination – these are some of the complicated forces that drive people up the ladder of success.

Some people naturally run out of steam at a certain point, accept their position, and set about finding fulfilment in other areas of life. But others become frustrated, despairing and resentful when they are not promoted to the jobs they yearn for and feel confident they can handle. They lose faith in themselves, their energy and motivation are eroded and they grow fearful of demotion or retrenchment.

Sometimes the opposite happens: a person is over-promoted into a post for which they lack the capabilities. They too labour under severe stress, afraid of being 'found out' and losing their job, overworking in an attempt to keep up.

STRESSBREAKERS

- Does your company encourage opportunities for career development? These could range from management training to computer skills and language lessons.
- Are there in-house training schemes or seminars you could join?
- Will your employers pay for or subsidise external courses?
- Talk to your boss or personnel department. Even if no schemes are currently available, your interest will be viewed positively.
- If necessary, apply for a course on your own initiative. If you're a freelance worker, you will have little other alternative. Further education colleges run day and evening courses in a wide variety of subjects.

THE END OF WORK

Unless you are moving on to something new and wonderful, leaving a job, whether through retirement or redundancy, is difficult. It involves a profound loss of identity and status after a lifetime of purpose, and people can find it hard to come to terms with their new role. Indeed, many cannot: the numbers of those succumbing to a fatal heart attack or cancer within a year or so of retirement is significantly high.

Relaxation techniques can help (see page 90) but don't hesitate to consult a professional counsellor if your company does not provide one.

BEGINNING A NEW JOB

New colleagues, a new routine, new corporate culture, new
expectations – these rate high on the life change scale, especially
if the climate at your new job is radically different from the one
you've left.

Louise returned to work in a publishing house after five years
at home with her young family. 'The first six months were
terrifying. I'd lost all concept of myself as an employee, as part of
a team, and office culture had become alien. I couldn't
understand the cues, worried about making mistakes, thought
everyone was criticising me and generally made mountains out of
molehills. Now I realise that, unless you really make a cock-up,
people are too busy getting on with their own jobs to notice.'

CHAPTER FIVE

You and your colleagues

Learning to live with other people is one of the most stressful aspects of life, according to stress researcher Dr Hans Selye: 'Good relationships between members of a group are a key factor in individual and organisational health.' When these break down, because of poor communication or ineffective management, people mistrust each other and the organisation, they lose interest in their work and outright hostility can erupt.

YOUR BOSS

A difficult relationship with your line manager is one of the biggest causes of stress at work. Not only is it bad for the company, but on a personal level it can smother your career. When the problem lies at top management level, it can be a formidable issue to address, and often infects the entire corporation.

Dr Peter Hanson, author of *The Joy of Stress* (Pan 1988) and *Stress for Success,* (Pan 1990) identifies 16 traits of 'bad' bosses. He or she:

1 *fuzzifies goals.* Staff have little idea what they should be doing and nothing is ever explained.

2 *can't delegate.* Employees are unable to develop responsibility or confidence.

3 *wastes the day in meetings.* Employees fall behind with their own workloads and have to catch up after hours or at home.

4 *has poor ethics.* A manager who fiddles his expenses or takes three-hour lunches can't expect loyalty and integrity from

staff. Working for a superior for whom you have little respect affects your own self-esteem.

5 *plays politics.* He or she picks favourites, passes over those who are most capable (and most threatening) and plays staff members off against each other.

6 *denies your personal life.* Workaholic or incompetent managers expect subordinates to put in the same punishing hours as they do. They'll telephone you unnecessarily at home and expect you to sacrifice your child's birthday party to turn up for an impromptu weekend meeting. They encourage the kind of climate where nobody dares leave the office before they do, and where employees play such infantile games as hanging their coat over their chair to establish their 'presence'.

7 *never says a word when you do something right.* No feedback, no compliments, no appreciation of a job well done – and certainly not in front of senior executives.

8 *always speaks up when you make a mistake* – especially in front of senior executives.

9 *always plays it 'by the book'.* There's no scope for creativity, lateral thinking or innovations – and heaven help you if you don't abide by the office dress code.

10 *works in splendour.* The 'peasants' make do with antiquated furniture while they surround themselves with antiques and executive loos.

11 *has a closed door policy.* It is impossible to schedule an appointment with him or her or get past the dragon of a secretary. Even if you manage to get into the sanctum, the secretary makes a point of interrupting.

12 *never listens to employees' or customers' complaints.*

13 *always imposes changes from the top down.* There's no consultation, even when changes will have a major impact on

employees' lives and careers. Then they wonder why morale is low.

14 *thinks all continuing staff education and training courses are a waste of money.*

15 *loves to push people to be workaholics.* People are a cost, not a resource, so why not work them until they drop.

16 *pays little attention to detail.* No thought is given to how or by whom something will be done, so long as it's off his or her desk.

Other than changing your job, there may be little you can do in such a situation apart from following the stress coping techniques in Part II. Complaining to Personnel or senior management can be diplomatically fraught although it is ultimately they who must confront the issue. Joining up with colleagues can label you a stirrer.

YOUR COLLEAGUES

A group of individuals will evolve a distinct culture which influences the behaviour of every member, more than any personality traits, according to social psychologists. In a company where the prevailing attitude is friendly and welcoming, it is easy to trust people and make friends. But if you join an organisation where the atmosphere is cold and competitive, you are likely to feel isolated and depressed – feelings that only the most determined extrovert can overcome. Your own reactions in turn contribute to the overall climate.

Personality clashes in this kind of combative environment can spawn seriously unpleasant behaviour. A recent survey revealed a surprisingly high degree of bullying in British workplaces. Not quite at playground beating level, but nasty verbal attacks and malicious tricks that were mentally and physically damaging for their victims.

Given the tendency for people working together to form natural affiliations, when two powerful individuals come into conflict, other staff can be forced into supporting factions, the worst kind of office 'politics'. Unless some resolution can be hammered out, the situation often results in one or the other protagonist leaving the company.

Even when antipathy between two people is contained, it is nonetheless deeply stressful. Max remembers working alongside a man for whom he developed a profound loathing. 'The intensity was absolutely irrational, though the basis was undoubtedly competitive. He was an outrageous sycophant and crawled round the manager who, to my disgust, appeared to be taken in by him. Everything this man did infuriated me; the way he sat, the way he talked on the phone, the way he blew his nose. We were in the same room so I had to look at him all day. I became obsessive about him and drove my wife and friends crazy with endless complaints. I was on the verge of handing in my resignation when fate stepped in. He was sacked for fiddling his expenses.'

On the up side, colleagues can become a kind of **surrogate family**. An older person might take on a parental role, advising junior staff on both work and personal dilemmas. Contemporaries seem like brothers and sisters. Friendships are forged from shared experiences that will endure throughout life. This kind of support is a powerful buffer against stress.

Work involvement like this also means greater job satisfaction, higher productivity, lower staff turnover and better relationships between managers and subordinates. People have a positive attitude towards their work; they come up with innovative ideas, voluntarily read relevant books and magazines, and willingly put in extra hours when necessary.

On the other hand, a study of American workers found that those who didn't (or couldn't) participate in their work culture were more likely to suffer from low self-esteem, low satisfaction with both their job and their life, escapist drinking and low motivation to work. They were readier to take days off work and talked frequently of leaving the job.

Many companies are aware of this and make concerted efforts to set up social programmes and encourage staff to meet each other. Discussion forums and in-house training programmes allow less formal and less hierarchical communication. The trend for personnel managers to be known as Directors of Human Resources is a reflection of corporate concern for good working relationships.

STRESSBREAKERS

- Be aware of the effect of your behaviour on other people. Ask for feedback – but be ready for a frank comment.
- If you're in a position of authority reward people for their efforts. Don't grunt; say thank you and look them in the eye.
- Be relaxed and positive with people. Smile and greet them by name. Make an effort to enquire about their personal life.
- Take the time to develop social relationships. Be proactive – ask a colleague to join you for lunch or an after-work drink.
- Respond positively to new ideas or requests. Don't always come up with reasons why something can't be done. And if you can't help, offer an alternative.
- If there are no interdepartmental social networks, approach Personnel. Be prepared to play a part in setting one up.

CHAPTER SIX

Stress and the working woman

If you're a working woman, there may be additional gender-based sources of stress.

The following conditions may be exacerbated by stress.

- amenorrhoea (loss of menstruation)
- premenstrual syndrome (PMS) – tension, irritability, headaches, depression
- postnatal depression
- menopausal mood swings, fatigue and depression
- painful intercourse
- inhibited sexual arousal
- inability to achieve orgasm
- infertility

The following are reported most frequently by women, but increasingly among men.

- anorexia nervosa
- bulimia

WHY IS WORK STRESSFUL FOR WOMEN?

Whether living with a partner or single, with or without children, for many women the workplace is an area of tension, conflict and resentment. There are numerous reasons, but the main factors are **fear of success** and **sexism,** according to American psychologist, Dr Georgia Witkin-Lanoil.

FEAR OF SUCCESS

Generally, girls and boys are brought up differently. Any biological and psychological differences between the sexes – and there is some evidence that boys may be innately more aggressive and tend to be better at spatial skills while girls outscore them verbally – will be compounded a thousand times by their conditioning. Even mothers who claimed total impartiality over their sons and daughters were found, when handed a strange infant, to respond according to the colour of its babysuit. They cuddled the blue baby less and allowed it to cry longer. The pink baby was talked to more, but was also told how pretty it was.

In a study of 110 different cultures by psychologists H. Barry, M. Bacon and I.L. Child:
- **82% of people expected females to be more nurturing than males**
- **87% expected females to be less achieving**
- **85% expected females to be less self-reliant.**

Many girls may grow up aware that to show anger, aggression or soaring ambition is considered unseemly and unfeminine, and likely to bring teasing and rebukes. As a result of trying to repress these natural impulses, young women on average suffer from higher **anxiety** levels than their brothers.

At work, this conditioning and anxiety has several outcomes.

Low expectations. Because women may feel that little is expected of them, they feel too inadequate to tackle anything more challenging and don't even try.

We're not talking only about young women who refuse to move out of the secretarial pool. Marietta went to an all-girls' school where she edited the school newspaper, produced plays and gained excellent A-levels. At university, in competition with men for the first time, she succumbed to gender stereotypes. Instead of pushing her natural strengths, she played a minor role on the student newspaper, achieved a middling degree and went into law. Eventually she became a solicitor specialising in divorce, although she had no great feeling for people's problems and always found libel law more fascinating. 'Women are better with family cases,' said her father, a judge. Her brother – whose school career was less distinguished academically – became a barrister. 'Libel's so complicated. I'd be out of my depth,' said Marietta. Her awareness that she had sold herself short niggled at her, however: a constant source of frustration and an erosion of self-esteem.

Fear of failure. Fear of success hinges on a fear of failure. Conforming to social expectations of appropriate behaviour is important to many people, and in a woman's case, these are proscribed by the (often antiquated) attitudes to women of the culture in which they work. If you put your head above the parapet, apply for managerial jobs, speak up in meetings and write cogent memos, you may get the spotlight but you also risk criticism, disappointment and – worse – shame. There's the general kind of sniping – 'Too big for her boots,' 'Who does she think she is,' 'No time for people's feelings' – and the more specific and destructive: 'I thought her report this morning lacked the necessary grasp of detail.'

Defensiveness. In many women, the fear of failure conflicts head-on with a natural hunger for achievement. Coping with this crucial source of stress leads to defensive behaviour. 'Women with a high fear of failure will constantly handicap themselves and increase their own stress in order to defend themselves against failure with excuses. For example, they may schedule too many things at the same time. Or they may never start a task until the last minute,' says psychologist Dr Georgia Witkin-Lanoil in *Coping with Stress – A Woman's Guide* (Sheldon 1990).

Difficulty in management. Because their upbringing may not have prepared them to be assertive or take control, women can run into genuine problems in managing other people. In trying to establish their authority, they may be aggressive and alienating. In their desperation to keep control of everything in their department, they are incapable of delegating work and responsibility. Not only does this affect their own efficiency, it breeds resentment among their subordinates.

Dependency. First their father, then their (real or anticipated) husband. Girls are encouraged and expected to be dependent on men, and it's a hard habit to break – especially if a woman has a supportive male boss who puts opportunities her way. The danger here – apart from the inevitable gossip and sexual innuendo – is that she can become identified with her mentor and find it difficult to establish an independent identity. She may be either embraced by his success or tainted by his failure.

STRESSBREAKERS

- Arm yourself with information, not opinions.
- Try not to see yourself as others see you.
- Ask yourself: do *I* want to achieve X or Y? (or is it my mother/father/partner/boss?)
- Remember that falling short of a goal is a learning experience, not a failure.
- Aim to do the job as well as possible, but don't blame yourself and don't seek praise.

Moving into management is particularly stressful for women, as this diagram illustrates (from *Living with Stress* by Cary L. Cooper, Rachel D. Cooper and Lynn H. Eaker)

Sources of stress		Sources of stress
Executive role expectations		Tiredness
'Patron' male boss		Anxiety attacks
Threatened male colleagues	**FEMALE**	Migraine headaches
Blocked promotion	**MANAGER**	Excessive drinking and/or smoking
Threat of sexual involvement		Irritation
		Tension (neck or back)
'Wonder Woman' syndrome managing home and work		Sleeplessness
		Frustration or dissatisfaction

Women executives should avoid becoming male clones and play to their strengths. Their natural management styles tend to be different from those of men – less authoritarian, more consultative – but just as effective and, in some cases, more so. The best are readier to muck in with staff and eschew perks that set them apart, according to researchers at the University of California. They often instinctively know one of the great lessons of leadership for men and women: by treating people as human beings rather than cogs in a machine, employees' self-interest can be translated into concern for group goals.

SEXISM

Virtually every working woman will encounter sexism at some time, in some form or another. It will range from the soft porn calendar in the foreman's office to seeing a less capable man installed in the senior management job she applied for. Her reactions will include anger, embarrassment, humiliation, loss of confidence and self-respect, insecurity and fear.

Male antipathy. A number of men – usually those who feel insecure and threatened in their jobs – enjoy putting down a woman colleague and generally making life awkward. Some professions are worse than others: anyone who watched Helen Mirren in *Prime Suspect* got a flavour of a woman's lot in the police force. Others proclaim equal opportunities for all – until a high-flying woman bumps her head against the invisible 'glass ceiling'. Or the dirty tricks department ensures that important background information never finds its way to her in time for a meeting; the 'lads' take to talking business in a men-only club.

Sexual harassment. Whatever else Political Correctness has done, sexual harassment is now an issue to be taken seriously. In fact, men are now claiming harassment by voracious women. But for every case that hits the headlines, there are thousands more where the offending actions may be so ambiguous, or the victim so intimidated, that no complaint is ever made. Take Adrienne, an unmarried television producer aged 33:

'With most guys it's a nuisance but you don't pay much attention. Stupid comments about your body, or voyeuristic enquiries about your love life. You just laugh and tell them to shove off. But I had an appalling situation with one of the editors. He's not unattractive but he's married and he has a reputation for being a bully.

'He took an interest in me and was very flattering – both about me personally and my work. At a recent conference we were staying in the same hotel and we had dinner together. I had several glasses of wine and became quite relaxed and talkative, and he was definitely flirtatious. He insisted on walking me to my room afterwards and tried to push his way in. When I said no, he got very ugly and threatening. He said I'd led him on, that I was sabotaging my career, that he'd see I never got anywhere. It was horrible and I was crying, but I managed to get inside and lock the door.

'Since then he's cut me dead, and I know he's saying things to people, criticising my work, picking up on any tiny mistake or omission. I applied for another post in the organisation recently, and one of his friends was on the interview panel. I really think I should have been a frontrunner, but I didn't get the job and I can't prove anything. It's only my word against his, and it would look like sour grapes. I don't know what to do.'

What to do if you are sexually harassed

- According to *The Sunday Times* charter against sexual harassment, sexual harrassment consists of any unwanted sexual conduct which is persistent and offensive. This includes sexual blackmail, uninvited touching and lewd comments, intimidation and displays of pornographic pictures.

- If you are offended by sexual innuendoes or approaches, make it clear that you don't appreciate such behaviour – though remember that work is a sociable place where people meet partners and what offends one person may not another. For example, according to a survey in *The Sunday Times*, professional women are readier to take offence than clerical staff.

- If you believe you are being sexually harassed, keep a note of the date and occasion of each incident.

● If possible, talk it over discreetly with other women colleagues. They may have had similar experiences and there's often strength in numbers.
● Establish whether your company has a sexual harassment policy for dealing with complaints.
● Seek informal and confidential advice from a woman in the workplace (usually in the Personnel Department) who has been appointed to deal with such complaints.
● Formal complaints should be lodged through a recognised grievance procedure.

THE ULTIMATE ROLE CONFLICT

The tension between traditional expectations of nurturing and achievement in a wider arena goes into the red when a working woman becomes 'A Mother', as we will see in Chapter Seven, Work, Home and Stress.

Work, home and stress

WHAT HAPPENS WHEN THE TWO WORLDS COLLIDE

Although not necessarily serious in themselves, the combined load of work and home stressors – especially the unexpected crisis – can be enough to make your stress bathtub overflow.

Stress has a way of leaking from one part of your life to another. Work stress will be carried home as fatigue, irritability and lack of judgement just as surely as any family or domestic difficulties will affect your job performance.

TAKING WORK STRESS HOME

If you are single and live alone, it may be difficult to defuse the day's anxiety. Stress is felt more acutely when you lack an emotional support system. What can happen when you leave the workplace is that you:

- sit at home and brood until your problems grow out of all proportion and everything seems worse
- can't be bothered preparing meals
- get drunk to escape
- resort to drugs

On the other hand, support systems can be abused. If you have a partner then you may:

- arrive home late because of overwork
- arrive home late because you've been drowning your sorrows

- take out your frustration on him/her/the children by losing your temper over minor domestic problems
- be uncommunicative because you are brooding over work
- ignore or forget family occasions
- fall asleep after supper because of fatigue and depression.

What can happen, in the worst scenario, is:

- you have an addiction problem
- your diet is inadequate and you get sick
- your relationship or marriage breaks up
- you lose contact with your children

Your behaviour inevitably becomes a source of stress for those you live with. 'Gavin's company nearly folded recently. His tossing and turning at night woke me up. I wanted to be sympathetic but lack of sleep made my first reaction one of resentment. Then I felt guilty. He was so miserable, but there was nothing I could do. If I asked him about it he pushed me off. I felt helpless and scared,' says his wife, Melanie.

Communication – talking to each other about what is happening and how you feel – is vital. (See page 103.) One woman consulted a marriage guidance counsellor, complaining that her husband treated her like a housekeeper and took her for granted. When he too came for counselling, it turned out that pressures at work had sapped his sexual drive. He was terrified that if he touched his wife she would expect sex and he wouldn't be able to perform. On hearing this, she wept. 'All I wanted was your arm around me. Nothing else,' she told him.

TAKING HOME STRESS TO WORK

The converse holds true as well; support at work can help an individual cope with sources of stress at home. Absenteeism, alcoholism, low productivity, low esteem and satisfaction, personality clashes – the effects of domestic unhappiness, such as a divorce or bereavement, on someone's performance at work are increasingly recognised, and a number of companies now employ counsellors to whom people can turn for confidential support and advice.

THE PARENT'S DILEMMA

Unquestionably, one of the greatest victims of work and home stress loads can be a working mother – especially if she is working full-time in a managerial position and her children are young. If she is single – and this also applies to single fathers caring for children – then the pressure of conflicting responsibilities may be almost intolerable.

Many organisations have taken on board the needs of working parents and provide company creches, subsidised childcare, paternity leave and parental leave and a returner programme for employees wishing to take time out while the children are young. The onset of the recession however means that in many cases only lip service is paid to these policies; it can be difficult to turn theory into fact.

Almost every working mother is afflicted by guilt to some degree, an insidious form of stress most keenly felt among those who are ambivalent about leaving their children but who are forced to work by financial constraints. She may suffer from anxiety, especially if she is not entirely happy about childcare arrangements, and from fatigue, which prevents her giving the family the attention she knows they need.

Ideally, both partners in a working couple should pull together, sharing the domestic chores. Unfortunately, this is not always the case. In a 1993 Mintel report, only about 1% of couples claimed to truly share housework and childcare. Men on average had an extra one to one-and-a-half extra hours of 'leisure' a day, and three hours at weekends. A high proportion of the men spent the time doing absolutely nothing.

Even when women shoulder much of the domestic burden, *emotional* support from their partner can count for a lot. Many working mothers report a great relief in knowing that someone will step into the breach if needs be.

'Stress is a late afternoon meeting that runs over time, a boss who doesn't approve of working mothers, a childminder who complains if you're not there on the dot, your husband's colleague coming for supper, football gear to be washed, a school project to be handed in and a 40-page business document to read by tomorrow,' says Elaine, personnel manager in a market research company.

STRESSBREAKERS

- Decide which chores you'd like to delegate and which you really want to keep for yourself. (This could be surprisingly hard for some women, who find they're more conditioned than they imagined to take responsibility for the home.)
- Ask for help. Explain that you feel overwhelmed and list the tasks you want taken over.
- This applies not only to your partner but to the children too. A six-year-old is capable of laying the table.
- If you can afford it, employ someone to clean the house or do the ironing.
- Don't cut corners with childcare. Your heart – and mind – won't be in your work if you're worrying about your children.

- When you're with the children, be with them, not with half a brain at tomorrow's conference. Your attention is even more precious than your time.

- When you get home, don't go straight into cooking supper. Sit down and talk to the family, or lie down and rest for 15–20 minutes.

- Read the chapters on relaxation, assertiveness and time management.

- Explore with your boss or personnel department the possibility of a more flexible arrangement – such as working from home one or two days a week or on a part-time basis.

- Liaise with other parents in your company who are in similar situations. Form a support group to share child-care arrangements or to lobby for better company policy.

- Contact Parents At Work/The Working Mothers Association for advice and support (see Resources for their address).

CHAPTER EIGHT

Wrong ways of coping

A life without stress would be dull beyond belief. Changes for good or ill are inevitable and, over the years most of us have developed our own ways of coping – partly governed by our personality and partly by previous experience. What worked once might, with any luck, work again.

The trouble is that our methods are often pretty piecemeal and ad hoc. We'll automatically plunge into the coping mode of our choice without considering whether this is the most appropriate way of dealing with the situation, or even if this particular problem is the real source of the stress. We could be barking up the wrong tree.

What we regard as coping can prove to be exactly the opposite: short-term knee-jerk reactions that actually make our stress worse.

IS YOUR PERSONALITY SABOTAGING YOU?

Your personality can influence not only what you find stressful, but your *symptoms* of stress – its physical and mental manifestations – as we saw in Chapter One. Hostile people may be at greater risk of heart disease, for instance, and anxious people of irritable bowel syndrome. But how does your personality determine the way you *cope* with stress?

Some types of people are more likely than others to find a situation stressful. This often has more to do with our past experiences, and particularly the way our parents brought us up, than with any traits we may have been born with. Anxious parents tend to produce anxious children. Those with critical parents may lack self-esteem and confidence.

'Every time I climbed a tree or wanted to walk myself to school, my mother would cry 'be careful', 'you'll be hurt,' 'there's a lot of nasty people about,'' says Margaret, a secondary school teacher, who expends a considerable amount of energy worrying over just about everything.

Margaret has what is known as an *external* Locus of Control. She sees herself as drifting through life with little influence or control over events. Things happen because of other people's decisions and actions, or simply because of chance or blind fate. 'There's nothing I can do,' she would say. 'It's out of my hands.'

Those who believe they are in control of events – like the 'hardy' personalities in Chapter One – handle difficulties with a minimum of angst. They possess an *internal* Locus of Control; inner resources which enable them to choose a modus operandi and take action. 'Let's see what can be done about this,' is their most likely comment.

Most of the time we are unaware of these subconscious thoughts colouring our reactions and ultimately affecting our health. Dr Robert S. Eliot, director of the Institute of Stress Medicine in Denver, devised the following test to discover the inner dialogue that determines your stress personality.

Circle the number that best reflects your response to the statement. 1 = never, 2 = sometimes, 3 = often, 4 = all the time

1	**I am exhausted by daily demands at work and home**	1 2 3 4
2	**My stress is caused by outside forces beyond my control**	1 2 3 4
3	**I am trapped by circumstances that I just have to live with**	1 2 3 4

4	No matter how hard I work to stay on top of my schedule, I can't catch up	1	2	3	4
5	I have financial obligations which I can't seem to meet	1	2	3	4
6	I dislike my work, but I can't take the risk of making a career change	1	2	3	4
7	I'm dissatisfied with my personal relationships	1	2	3	4
8	I feel responsible for the happiness of people around me	1	2	3	4
9	I am embarrassed to ask for help	1	2	3	4
10	I do not know what I want out of life	1	2	3	4
11	I am disappointed that I have not achieved what I had hoped for	1	2	3	4
12	No matter how much success I have, I feel empty	1	2	3	4
13	If the people around me were more competent, I would feel happier	1	2	3	4
14	People let me down	1	2	3	4
15	I stew in my anger rather than express it	1	2	3	4
16	I become enraged and resentful when I am hurt	1	2	3	4
17	I can't take criticism	1	2	3	4
18	I am afraid I'll lose my job (home, finances, etc)	1	2	3	4
19	I don't see the value of expressing sadness or grief	1	2	3	4
20	I don't trust that things will work out	1	2	3	4

Scoring. 20–29 = Excellent. You have a high degree of control, self-esteem and identity. 30–49 = Good. You have a healthy sense of control over your life, but occasionally negative self-talk makes you feel anxious in stressful situations. Try thinking more positively: 'I can do it'. 50–69 = Fair. Your opinions are often clouded and you feel trapped because of frequent negative self-talk. Think more positively. Beware of negative thoughts condemning yourself and others that have no basis in reality. Don't expect perfection. 70–80 = Poor. Life is a struggle from one crisis to another. Consider seeing a therapist if you can't get a handle on your negative self-talk. Cognitive therapy, which helps you change your thought patterns, is very helpful.

[Taken from *From Stress to Strength: How to Lighten Your Load and Save Your Life* by Robert S. Eliot (Bantam).]

HOW DO DIFFERENT PERSONALITIES HANDLE STRESS?

Every individual is unique, and it may be difficult to place yourself in any one category. At a rough guess, however:

If you are **anxious** you may:

● feel reluctant to discuss your problems with other people in case you appear incompetent or ignorant

● work yourself into a state of nervousness, fear and/or panic

Action: Bite the bullet and seek a sympathetic ear. Reassurance will transform your view of everything

If you are **obsessional** you may:

● allow your problems to preoccupy you to the exclusion of everything else

● go over and over them until everybody is fed up with listening to you

● feel your control of daily routine is slipping because of your constant fretting and therefore...

● develop compulsive behaviour patterns, such as repeatedly checking that gas and electrical appliances are turned off, windows are locked, and – in severe cases – complicated rituals such as washing your hands continuously for fear of contamination

Action: Because you can't sort out which worry is worse than another, sit down and make a list of them in order of priority.

If you are **introspective** you may:

● examine and re-examine events from every conceivable angle
● allow stress to get out of proportion because you have dwelt on the worst possible scenario

Action: Find a sympathetic listener, who will help you sort out the mental confusion in which you've landed yourself.

If you are **withdrawn** you may:

● avoid stress by detaching yourself from involvement with other people and events
● create a fantasy world in which everything is rosy

Action: Make a real effort to communicate with other people.

If you are **suspicious** you may:

● believe that the world is earmarked with perils for you
● suspect other people of intending you malice and harm
● blame others for your problems
● see any support or advice as a threat
● treat refusals as a personal rejection

Action: However difficult, try to trust people when they offer help. Make an effort to imagine yourself in other people's shoes and offer help in return.

If you are **placid and dependent** you may:

● let problems roll over you without attempting to deflect or resolve them.

Action: When people offer advice try to follow their suggestions. Better still, take the initiative instead of relying on others to bail you out.

If you are **aggressive and hostile** you may:

● ignore other people's feelings thus making situations worse
● oppose things because you don't know how else to react
● reject advice if you don't agree with it

Action: Unfortunately you're unlikely to pay attention to any suggestions until some catastrophe has humbled you enough to listen.

STRESSBREAKERS

What you can do:
- *Talk it out.* Share it with someone else. Others will welcome your trust.
- *Write it out.* It is easier to see a problem in perspective when it is put on paper.
- *Shrug it off.* Raise your shoulders then drop them. Relax your body.
- *Breathe it away.* Inhale deeply and exhale heavily a few times. Calm your thoughts.
- *Sort it out.* List practical options, weigh them up, make a decision, then act.
- *Delay it.* Put aside 15 minutes a day for a worry session; leave it until then.
- *Work it off.* Do something physical. Clear your head, divert your energy.
- *Reverse it.* Consider taking an opposite approach, explore alternatives.

How you can behave:
- *Laugh it off.* Lighten it with humour. Be generous with smiles.
- *Distance it.* Imagine a few years from now. How much will it matter then?
- *Balance it.* Consider the good consequences and feel glad about them.
- *Cancel it.* Think positively, don't let the negative pull you down.
- *Exaggerate it.* Picture the worst that could really happen. Is it likely?

- **Win through it.** Imagine yourself being successful and feel good about it.
- **Hold it.** Say 'Stop', pause, and think. Now take a fresh look.
- **Escape it.** Notice something enjoyable around you. Get into the present.

(From HEA Look After Your Heart: Look After Yourself)

ARE YOU TRAPPED BY BAD HABITS?

The previous chapters may have helped you identify the sources of your stress. The next step is to consider the ways in which you are currently trying to deal with it. You are likely to be digging yourself even deeper into the mire if you recognise any of the following.

Denial. A refusal to admit that anything is wrong in the hope that it will go away. Often it does not; in fact it will probably get worse.

Escapism. Moving from one situation to another – a new job, a new marriage – in an attempt to make a 'fresh start' and leave problems behind. But as it's the way you habitually behave that is usually the problem, your troubles travel with you.

Avoidance. Arranging your life so that you avoid stressful situations – or indeed, any kind of challenge that might be uncomfortable in the short run. As you're always cancelling appointments it puts a strain on your personal and business relationships.

Projection. You blame everyone but yourself for whatever goes wrong. It's your partner's fault the car is out of petrol even though you drove it last. Your proposal wasn't accepted because the client didn't brief you thoroughly.

Displacement. Feelings of aggression and frustration are dumped on other people (usually those who know and love you best) and things, i.e. rather than punching an awkward customer you thump the desk when they've gone.

Rationalisation. A classic case of self-deception. You explain away your conduct with any number of plausible reasons – except the real ones. For example, you haven't completed a report on time – not because you kept putting it off (the real reason) but because you were awaiting the results of a (possibly) relevant conference.

Nostalgia. Things were better in the past. You avoid present stresses by contemplating past happiness and success.

Regression. When stress is very severe, people may escape by reverting to childhood behaviour. They were dependent on others then to protect them and order their life.

Repression. Sometimes we bury past traumas in our unconscious and forget they ever happened. But the weight of them is still with us, and when we find ourselves in a similar situation or our current stress levels are very heavy, they can surface as nightmares, depression, phobias and obsessions.

ADDICTIVE WAYS OF COPING WITH STRESS

The Workaholic. Not to be confused with the genuine *work enthusiast* who works hard but enjoys it and knows when to stop and find time for other things. Overworking is often not so much the result of real work overload, but an ineffective way of coping with stress, a despairing 'if-I-keep-running-I'll-just-about-manage-to-stay-on-top' behaviour. These people are driven by anxiety, a desperation to claw some kind of control over a life that is besieged on all fronts.

For some, workaholism is an addiction. They may be in the office from 8am to 8pm, but time is wasted fiddling about, talking, sitting in meetings (organised by workaholic bosses) and arranging ego-stroking lunches. By late afternoon panic sets in, triggering the necessary adrenaline surge that will keep them at their desks finishing work hours after any sane person has gone home.

Anybody who works to deadlines knows how hard it is to summon up commitment early in the piece, how seductive and exciting is the last minute rush, burning the midnight oil, hurtling about at the eleventh hour to deliver the finished product, and how satisfying is the afterglow, when it's all done and gone. It's an artificially created stress that derives from poor time management and a fear of boredom.

Whatever thrills the workaholic gets from this – dubious as they complain mightily of stress – it puts unwelcome and unnecessary pressure on those about them. Personal relationships and family life suffer because they are never home or, when they are, are closeted with papers. Subordinates suffer; a workaholic boss doesn't believe staff are putting in a day's work unless, like him, they're still in the office when the cleaners are knocking at the door.

Others resort to workaholism as an escape – from loneliness, from an unhappy relationship, from depression, from fear of facing themselves and their inadequacies. Work may be the only place where they feel in some control of their personal chaos, or where people seem to appreciate them. A frantic and vicious circle ensues: the more they run from emotional stress the more physical stress they engender, until they finally succumb to so-called 'executive burnout'; physical and psychological exhaustion which may so destroy their health that they can never work again.

The Smoker. The greater the stress, the more cigarettes a smoker will puff. And yet the chemical changes that nicotine produces in the body includes the release of stress hormones adrenaline and noradrenaline. Smoking actually makes stress symptoms worse. Worrying about your smoking is stressful, but so is trying to stop – although it will be better for you in the long run.

The Drinker. When you can't get through a minor crisis during the day without resorting to alcohol, then you should think seriously about your dependency on drink. As it's a sedative, not a stimulant, it will only serve to dull the memory and concentration.

It used to be said that men traditionally reached for the bottle when under stress from work, and women when their relationships were threatened. Such gender differentiations are being eroded, however. As women move into management, they are copying their male counterparts in resorting to alcohol as a coping mechanism. Some occupations seem to place people in more temptation than others: doctors, publicans and journalists all have high death rates from cirrhosis of the liver.

The Drug Taker. The drug-induced 'high' and the escape from everyday miseries that it brings can be a temptation to return for more. If it becomes an addiction, it will damage your job performance and your personal relationships, and the quest for money to feed your habit will be an additional source of stress.

STRESSBREAKER

Encourage a sense of humour in yourself and those around you. Laughter releases endorphins, the body's natural painkillers, and creates a sense of well-being. Even black humour can help you maintain a sense of perspective in the bleakest situations. Sharing jokes with colleagues makes the workplace happier and fosters motivation.

CHAPTER NINE

Take care of your body

ARE YOU GETTING ENOUGH REST?

Everything seems overwhelmingly bad when you are tired. Concentration slips, the irritability threshold is low and little hurdles you would normally take in your stride turn into insurmountable barriers. The first thing to do, in the short term, is to make sure you're getting enough rest.

Take a walk. The fresh air will clear your head, nature will rejoice your spirit, the activity will stimulate you and breaking free from your desk will give you a new perspective.

Take a nap. Any number of people swear by 15 or 20 minutes catnapping, preferably after lunch when energy levels are at their natural low. The Mediterranean custom of the siesta makes physiological sense. Admittedly a nap is not easy to manage in a busy open-plan office, but those working from home or in their own offices might be more successful.

Get away for the weekend. A literal escape from reminders of daily pressures can be a real tonic and provide a chance to stand outside yourself. Somehow those 'must read' documents look a little less urgent when there are cows outside the window.

Have a good night's sleep. Heavy workloads and deadlines may mean skimped sleep, getting by night after night with an hour or two less than you really need. Yet a good night's rest can stop that stress bathtub from overflowing, and add a gloss to the greyest of circumstances. Solutions to the knottiest problems suddenly present themselves out of the blue.

As insomnia is a major symptom of stress, this may be easier said than done. If it's also a *source* of stress for you, bear in mind that when tested in sleep laboratories, many self-claimed insomniacs were actually unconscious for large parts of the night and were getting more rest than they realised.

The minimum amount of sleep to function normally is six hours, according to sleep expert Professor Jim Horne of Loughborough University. Everyone has different requirements and the notion of eight hours a night is a myth. In fact, one of the current cures for insomnia is to limit the time in bed to six hours a night; exhaustion finally ensures the patient sleeps throughout.

People with sleep problems fall into three patterns: those who can't fall asleep when they get into bed; those who wake frequently during the night; and those who wake early and can't go back to sleep. The last is the most commonly associated with stress.

Nodding-off tips

- **Keep off caffeine from midday onwards.**
- **Avoid excessive alcohol. It can wake you later in the night.**
- **Don't smoke. Nicotine raises blood pressure and pulse rate.**
- **Avoid digesting a heavy meal within two to three hours of bedtime**
- **A bedtime snack of warm milk, wholemeal biscuits and/or a banana contains sleep-promoting amino acids and carbohydrates.**
- **Herbal remedies such as valerian, lavender, camomile and hop pillows can be effective.**

- Be active and exercise during the day – but as a rule not too strenuously within an hour or two of bedtime. Sex is one of the exceptions, as it leaves you relaxed.
- Keep regular bedtime hours. Late nights are the equivalent of jet lag.
- Keep your bedroom calm and comfortable. Avoid extremes of heat or cold; when dreaming the body can't self-regulate temperature.
- Don't lie in bed fretting. Get up and do something else until you feel drowsy.
- If dawn light wakes you in summer, get heavier curtains or wear an eye mask.
- Practise relaxation and visualisation techniques (see page 90.)

EAT WELL

One of the first standards to slip when you're under pressure – whether good or bad – is diet. Our bodies, rather like cars, perform better when they are given the right kind of fuel in the right amounts. When you're working flat out and think you haven't time to stop and eat, a cup of coffee for breakfast and a jam doughnut for lunch won't exactly spark a high octane performance. Without sufficient nutrients, our body systems lack energy, muscles tire, the brain flags and the immune system's defences are down. Because our coping mechanisms are under par, stress comes at us like a juggernaut.

A healthy diet can be summed up in some simple rules based upon the five food groups.

- Eat lots of bread, other cereals and potatoes. Other cereals include breakfast cereals, pasta, rice, oats, noodles, and cornmeal. Beans and pulses can be eaten as a part of this group.

- Eat lots of fruit and vegetables. Fresh, frozen and canned fruit and vegetables, dried fruit and fruit juice can all contribute. Beans and pulses can also be eaten as part of this group.

- Eat or drink moderate amount of milk and dairy foods – choosing lower fat versions where you can. (Note: butter, eggs and cream are included in the fatty and sugary foods group, and not here.)

- Eat moderate amounts of meat, fish and alternatives (such as pulses and beans) – choosing lower fat versions where you can.

- Eat fatty and sugary foods sparingly, either infrequently or in small amounts or both.

Nutritionists argue over the necessity for **food supplements,** but generally agree that a balanced diet is preferable with a range of foods eaten from the groups above in the correct proportions. Exceptions include women with heavy periods who may need iron supplements, and smokers who use up vitamin C faster than non-smokers.

Antioxidant vitamins C, E and beta carotene (A) are thought to offer protection against cancer and heart disease because they scavenge 'free radicals'. These are molecules that are produced constantly in the body and exist for only a few seconds – but long enough to damage DNA, the genetic material in the cells, and trigger chain reactions in the arteries which could lead to heart attacks and other health problems. Chemicals, cigarette smoke, industrial pollution and radiation are also blamed for creating free radicals.

Food sources of vitamin A include liver, butter, cheese, margarine, eggs and oily fish. Carrots, tomatoes, apricots, spinach and broccoli are good sources of beta-carotene which the body converts to Vitamin A. Vitamin C is found in such foods as oranges and other citrus fruits, blackcurrants, strawberries, kiwi fruit, tomatoes, spinach and other dark green vegetables, mango and papaya. Sources of vitamin E are nuts, vegetable oils, whole grains, olives, asparagus, spinach, tinned salmon and tuna in oil, eggs, avocado, muesli, blackberries, wholemeal bread and brown rice.

Some experts argue that our environment is so polluted that even a balanced diet cannot provide enough antioxidants and recommend supplements. Care should be taken as overdosing on vitamin A can cause birth defects in unborn children, harms the liver and causes blurred vision and headaches. Most supplements provide it in the form of its harmless precursor, beta carotene.

Go easy with **caffeine.** A cup of coffee in the morning improves concentration and gives you a lift, but cup after cup can make your heart race and cause irritability, depression and insomnia.

BE ACTIVE

Studies show that stress levels are lower in fit people who are physically active. Regular exercise not only helps regulate weight, keep muscles toned, heart rate low and blood pressure within the normal range; it also gives a psychological boost. Apart from the sense of achievement that comes from a trim body, exercise stimulates the release of opiate hormones called endorphins that give feelings that some people describe as a 'high'.

Yet an estimated 80% of the population is unfit. Many people say they find exercise boring and there are often no instant rewards – it can take a minimum of eight to twelve weeks for benefits to be noticeable.

On the other hand, you don't have to spend strenuous hours in a gym to become fit. Aim for 30 minutes of moderate activity on most days of the week, and 15–60 minutes of aerobic exercise (enough to make you puff) three to five days a week. Including relaxation techniques in the schedule, such as listening to music or yoga and t'ai chi ch'uan movements, has been found to enhance mood and reduce anxiety as well.

You can build physical activity into your daily routine. Walk to the railway station, climb stairs rather than take the lift. If you're taking up a sport, choose one that is not too competitive: the pressure to win may only add to your stress levels.

Aerobic forms of exercise include:
- **cycling**
- **dancing**
- **running and jogging**
- **skiing – especially cross-country**
- **swimming**
- **tennis and badminton**
- **walking – simplest and cheapest.**

Remember
- Set sensible goals. If you're out of condition, begin with a few minutes of exercise three times a week and work up to 15 to 30 minutes of physical activity on most days.

- Check with your doctor if you suffer from high blood pressure, dizziness, heart disorders, back pain, diabetes, arthritis, or if you're over 45 and concerned that you may have problems if you start to be more active.
- Choose a convenient form of exercise or activity that doesn't involve complicated equipment and travelling.
- Wear appropriate footwear and clothing.
- Vary the exercise. Walk one day, cycle the next.
- Stop and rest if you feel dizzy. You shouldn't exercise so hard that you can't hold a conversation at the same time.
- Spend five or ten minutes warming up beforehand and winding down afterwards if activity is vigorous.

CHAPTER TEN

Take stock of your life

By now you probably have some idea of what is stressful for you, and possibly why. Whether you can cope with it is another matter. If you feel swamped by what's happening in your life rather than in control and able to deal with whatever is thrown at you, it's easy to slide into a perpetuating downward spiral of depression and disrupted sleep. A holiday or weekend break may afford some relief, but once you step back into the workplace on Monday the whole pile of horrors rises up to greet you. It's a well-known medical observation, confirmed by Harvard Medical School research, that more heart attacks occur between eight and nine o'clock on Monday mornings than any other time of the week.

When people are caught up in this kind of treadmill, taking time out to contemplate the state of their life seems madness, an impossibility. Stress can devour every corner of your being, leaving no inner spaces for renewal, and ultimately burnout may be the only, and most drastic, way out. Yet a few hours could be sufficient to forestall the downhill plummet.

Get away somewhere – an hour's drive into the country could be enough, so long as the atmosphere is unlike that of your work or home – and, armed with pen and paper, take stock of your life. The act of putting your thoughts down in black and white is important (some would argue that the neural connection between brain and hand is the key) and remains a reference for the future.

WHERE ARE YOU NOW?

There are several exercises designed to help you clarify your priorities and the life goals you want to set yourself. One of the simplest is a pie chart.

Think of the various components of your life. Apart from work, there may be partner, family, friends, commuting and travel, community work (helping with the school fête, collecting for charity, doorstepping for the local political party), leisure, education and spiritual development.

Draw a circle like a pie, and divide it into slices, each slice representing the amount of time you give to the components listed above. Let the pie represent how your life *is* right now. You may find, for instance, that you have a hankering to learn French (education) but haven't found the opportunity to start. Draw it as a thin sliver – you *are* at least thinking about it.

Some questions you might ask yourself are:

● Would I like to spend more time with the family?
● Am I spending too much time commuting?
● When did my partner and I last talk together about our dreams and feelings?
● Am I spending too much time at work in tasks I don't enjoy?
● Do I have leisure interests that take me out of my work mode?
● When did I last read a book for fun, or go to the theatre?
● Have I played sport or walked in the country in the last six months?
● When did I last have a good laugh?

Now draw another chart and this time make the slices the sizes you would like them to be in a perfect world. Suppress any little voice that says 'impractical' or 'impossible'.

Compare the two charts. What could be done to make the first match the second? You might, for instance, find that work occupies a huge chunk of Pie Chart One, so that family and leisure is squeezed smaller than you'd like and community work is no more than a line. This imbalance probably accounts for a lot of your stress. The support system you need is clearly lacking.

Keep your charts and at regular periods repeat the exercise. Nothing in life is stable and as you and your circumstances develop, both charts will change.

WHERE DO YOU WANT TO BE?

Set yourself life goals. Using the same headings as in the pie chart, write down what you'd like to be doing in each sector in a week. Then in a month, in six months, in a year, in three years, in five years' time. Include your dreams, no matter how simple or far-fetched. A happy gardener? A successful film producer? Why not.

Place three stars beside those that are really important to you. Two stars beside the quite important ones, and one star beside the it'll-be-nice-if-it-happens ones. Now ask yourself which are achievable and which are not.

If you fancy being a film producer on the strength of reading an article about Steven Spielberg's millions you might lack the obsessional fascination for film making that drives those in the business. On the other hand, if watching movies is your passion, then a course in film making might be a start. Do you qualify for a grant? How would you make the time? Do you belong to a film club? List the pros and cons, and all the information and changes needed – in your job, your relationships, your leisure time.

On your life plan, then, the first week's goal might be to investigate what filmmaking courses are available. The five year action plan: to have completed your first film. When set out like this, vague ambitions have a way of gaining structure and reality.

Midlife can be a time of stress for many men and women. Your career seems to have peaked and all is decline and wrinkles from now on. Rubbish. If you want to be partner in the firm or managing director, write it down, but look very hard at what is needed. Would it mean sacrifices that you are not prepared to make? Are there other desirable goals that may not involve high status and financial success, but the achieving of which could transform your life?

WHAT ARE YOUR POSITIVES?

List your achievements and advantages. What are your strong points? Are you a good organiser? Add any compliments that you have received.

WHAT ARE YOUR NEGATIVES?

Some experts recommend making a list of areas for improvement and finding a positive angle to each of them. 'Aggressive' could become 'decisive;' or 'anxious' become 'careful'. How can you reduce the former and enlarge the latter?

WHAT ARE YOUR VALUES?

Describe your own funeral. Who will be there and what will they say about you? If you had six months to live but remained in the same circumstances you are in now, what changes might you make in your behaviour? Macabre, perhaps, but an effective way of focussing on what really matters to you.

We all have a set of beliefs that colours the way we measure other people and events and influences decisions about how we spend our time and money. Some will have been spoon-fed into us in childhood and we've barely given them a thought. Others will result from our own experiences and those of our friends.

These beliefs form our value system – what we hold to be good and bad, right and wrong. If the situation in which we find ourself, our job or our relationships, is out of kilter with these attitudes, then we literally feel de-valued. Even when unacknowledged (because to do so consciously might threaten our status quo) the misfit is a nagging and destabilising source of strain. But if one builds on the fundamentals of fairness, honesty and integrity that most of us recognise, then our values are enhanced and become a wellspring of energy.

Liz Willis from the Springboard Training Programme suggests making four lists of the things you value: at work, in relationships, the world and yourself. Check where they are in agreement and where they conflict. Under work, you may have written 'making money' or 'fame'. But how will these square with 'bringing up a family' or 'an end to world hunger?'

Rank your values in terms of 'I *must* have,' 'I would like to have,' and 'It would be nice to have.' Tick those that are being met and underline those that are not. Regard any unfulfilled values in the 'must have' list as clues for future goals.

CHAPTER ELEVEN

Self-help techniques

BREATHING

Considering we breathe around 20,000 times a day and if we didn't we'd be dead, it's astonishing how many people are not very good at it. When we're tense and anxious, we tend to breathe rapidly, using the upper part of the chest. This is fine if you're exercising – or want to fight or run away – but if maintained causes hyperventilation (not enough oxygen coming in and too much carbon dioxide being expelled) which can lead to panic attacks. Even at the best of times, most people only use half their lung capacity, which means that insufficient oxygen is absorbed into the lungs and too much carbon dioxide is left in the tissues and blood.

Slow diaphragmatic breathing is one of the most effective ways of managing stress. It uses the diaphragm (the sheet of muscle between the chest cavity and the abdomen) to allow efficient expansion of the lungs, and the kind of relaxed breathing as in sleep. This ensures adequate supplies of oxygen to the body without expelling too much carbon dioxide, a substance the blood needs in just the right amount to maintain its optimum level of acidity.

When breathing in, the diaphragm contracts downwards, causing the abdomen to rise and the lungs to expand. Breathe out and the diaphragm relaxes, making the abdomen and lungs contract, expelling air.

To check that you are using abdominal breathing:

● Lie down or sit comfortably with your eyes closed.

● Place one hand on your chest and the other on your abdomen at the lower edge of your ribs. Notice which hand moves when you breathe.

● If the hand on your chest moves your breathing is too shallow.

● Place both hands on your abdomen and inhale and exhale slowly. As you breathe in deeply, feel the diaphragm move out and down, your abdomen rise and your ribs expand up and out. Your fingers should move up and apart.

● Breathe out smoothly, and feel your abdomen fall and your diaphragm and ribs relax.

● Continue practising. Allow the deep breathing to become more natural, but check that your stomach is still rising and falling.

Checkpoints. Ensure that your shoulders are not moving up and down with your breathing. Some people haul air into their lungs in this way.

Feeling faint or heady is usually due to flushing out too much carbon dioxide. Breathe calmly and naturally for a few minutes until the sensation passes.

RELAXATION

Being able to relax at will is the best possible way of dealing with stress; it lowers the blood pressure, breathing and metabolic rate and slows the heartbeat, enabling the body's systems to recover from over-arousal.

When we are stressed and under pressure, our muscles tense and become tight and stiff – which in turn contributes to headaches, aches and pains and fatigue. Basic relaxation allows you to release muscular tensions associated with breathing.

1   Choose a time when you haven't just finished a heavy meal.

2   Make sure your clothes are loose and comfortable and your feet covered for warmth.

3   Ensure the room is warm and that you won't be disturbed for at least 15 minutes.

4   Either sit comfortably with your feet supported or lie on your back on a firm bed or mat on the floor. Place a thin cushion or paperback book under your head and/or thighs if you feel uncomfortable. Your head, body and legs should be in a straight line, your shoulders eased a little lower, your feet flopped outwards and your hands resting gently by your side.

5   Slowly close your eyes and sigh to release tension. Let the floor take your body weight.

6   Pay attention to the rhythm of your own breathing. Notice the fall and rise of your abdomen. Try to breathe a little more slowly. Emphasise the breath out, before breathing in again.

7   As you breathe out more slowly be aware of a pause before you breathe in again.

8   Release tension in your toes and legs. Some people find it helps to silently say 'relax and let go.'

9   Release tension in your fingertips, through to your forearms and the upper arms. Notice the sensations as you release the tension. Some people feel warm and heavy, others light and floaty.

10 Ease tension in your shoulders by lowering them and find a comfortable position for your head.

11 Calm down the muscles of your face. Mentally smoothe out the muscles of your forehead and relax the muscles around your eyes. Release the muscles around your mouth and let your jaw go loose. Find a comfortable position for your tongue in your mouth, not too far forward or too far back.

12 Now notice the rhythm of your own breathing pattern again. Try to breathe out more slowly and be aware of a second's pause before breathing in again.

13 As you lie there, be aware of the feeling of relaxation in your muscles.

14 When you are ready, wriggle your toes and fingers. You may like to push your heels away from the body to gently stretch the backs of the legs.

15 Gently ease your back and, in your own time, open your eyes.

16 You may want to stretch.

17 In your own time, very gently bend your knees and roll on to one side for a while before slowly getting up.

When you first do this exercise, you may only feel fully relaxed for a few moments, but frequent practice makes it easier and prevents the build-up of unnecessary muscle tension. Try to practise this relaxation technique for two ten-minute sessions a day. One session before bed will ensure a better night's sleep; the other can be whenever you want – even sitting in the train or at your desk in the office.

(Relaxation exercise adapted from the HEA Look After Your Heart: Look After Yourself programme)

STRESSBREAKER

To release tension quickly in a difficult situation:

Calm and control your breathing by taking two or three deeper, slower outbreaths. Return to normal breathing. Then repeat the two or three deeper, slower outbreaths. Carry on more calmly.

When the situation can't be changed, give a 'mental shrug': sigh; drop your shoulders; tell yourself 'who cares'.

VISUALISATION

Harnessing the mind – in this case, the creative power of the imagination – is a powerful way to relax the body. If these exercises seem a bit daft, don't worry; take the time to practise them properly and they will work.

Find a quiet place, lie down or make yourself comfortable in an easy chair, close your eyes, take a deep breath and let go.

Imagine a calm and beautiful scene, somewhere that you find relaxing and peaceful. It might be a beach, or a mountain valley: a place that you have visited, or a picture you have seen in a book or film. In your mind, feel the ground – the scrunch of sand, perhaps, the soft scratchiness of grass, the soothing stroke of carpet. Smell the scents, listen to the sounds.

If your mind wanders, bring it gently back to the image. Repeat phrases known as 'positive affirmations': 'I feel peaceful.' 'I am relaxed and content.'

Use visualisation to carry you through high-pressure situations at work. For a few days before, say, an important meeting or presentation, relax and picture the room or auditorium full of the people who will be there.

Run through the programme in your mind. If you feel tension rising at the thought of a potential difficulty, breathe, relax and detach yourself from the scene. As an observer, watch yourself standing in front of the audience, speaking lucidly and calmly. Watch the people listening, paying attention. Hear the applause and congratulations as you finish.

MEDITATION

For many Westerners, meditation's association with gurus and Eastern mysticism has made it rather suspect. In fact, scientific research has shown that the technique is a highly effective way of decreasing blood pressure and breathing rate, slowing the heartbeat and lowering the metabolic rate to levels not found outside very deep sleep or hibernation. The brain wave frequency changes to the long alpha waves that are a sign of deep relaxation coupled with a state of mental alertness.

Far from being other-worldly, regular meditators seem to develop greater powers of concentration and control over their lives. They also appear more mentally flexible and receptive to new ideas.

The practice is not confined to the East. Christian and Jewish mystic traditions have long had sophisticated techniques for withdrawing from ordinary consciousness, in their case to contact God. Religious faith, however, is not mandatory for meditation – although when it becomes a regular habit it can lead to spiritual growth and moments of profound fulfilment.

Various schools of meditation have rules about what position to adopt and which mental exercises to perform, but Dr Herbert Benson of Harvard Medical School, who has carried out extensive research into relaxation and meditation, found that anybody can achieve a state of relaxed awareness by following four basic provisos:

1 A quiet environment.
2 A comfortable position, usually sitting so as to prevent sleep or drowsiness.
3 An object to focus the attention on (such as the breath or a mantra, the repetition of a particular word or phrase) so that the mind's chattering can be ignored.
4 Passive awareness or mindfulness (see below).

If it's difficult to discipline yourself at first, join a meditation class. They are sometimes advertised in local libraries and health centres.

How to meditate

1 Find a place where you won't be disturbed.

2 Make sure the room is warm and your clothes comfortable.

3 If possible, practise for 15 to 20 minutes twice a day, before a meal. If you must keep an eye on the time, open an eye occasionally to check a strategically placed clock, rather than setting an alarm which could give a rude awakening.

4 A cross-legged lotus pose is not obligatory. Sit on an upright chair, back comfortably straight, feet firmly on the ground or a support, hands in your lap or on your knees, palms either up or down. Imagine a straight line aligning your navel with the tip of your nose, or a string pulling you up from the crown of your head. Close your eyes and relax.

5 Breathe rhythmically and slowly through your nose and down into your abdomen.

6 Focus on the object of your meditation. This could be your breath, observing it go in and out as you count to four; or an image, such as a candle flame or a flower, to hold in your mind; or a word or phrase to repeat. Many people use 'peace' or 'one'.

7 When your mind wanders, don't fret but gently draw it back to the object of meditation.

8 At the end, take a full minute to return slowly to everyday life. Open your eyes and become fully aware of your surroundings. Stretch and move your limbs about before getting up. Your blood pressure will have dropped so don't leap suddenly to your feet.

MINDFULNESS

Regular meditation encourages mindfulness, the essence of psychologist Dr Jon Kabat-Zinn's celebrated programme at the Stress Reduction Clinic, University of Massachusetts Medical Centre, USA. He describes it as allowing yourself to be in the present moment 'with things exactly as they are, without trying to change anything;' noting what passes through your attention and letting it go.

This enables us to calm down and *see* how we're living and what changes to make. We can channel energy more effectively into stressful situations or when we feel threatened, and because this energy comes from within, it is always within our reach and control.

As an introduction to mindfulness, Dr Kabat-Zinn gives everybody three raisins, to be eaten one at a time, paying attention to what they are doing and experiencing from moment to moment. They observe the raisin as if they've never seen one before, feel its texture, notice its colours, note any thoughts they might be having about raisins in general. Then they smell it, bring it to their lips, aware of how their arm moves to do so and their mouth salivates in anticipation. This process continues while chewing and swallowing the raisin and even to imagining their bodies to be one raisin heavier.

Mindfulness, he says, can be practised in all our waking moments, not only while sitting in meditation. You can take out the garbage mindfully, eat mindfully, drive mindfully. 'We learn to be aware of our fears and pain, yet at the same time stabilised and empowered by a connection to something deeper within ourselves,' he says.

YOGA

Yoga is proving therapeutic in restoring energy and treating stress-related conditions. It combines stretching exercises, considered essential for fitness in sports medicine, and breathing, relaxation and meditation techniques.

Yoga (the word means 'union' in Sanskrit and has the same root as the English 'yoke') has been practised in India for 6,000 years. The spiritual, mental and physical exercises were designed to bring the practitioner into harmony with higher consciousness, but Western teachers are bringing fresh insights to the ancient techniques.

Ideally you should begin with a teacher to make sure you're on the right path; then daily practice will help reap further benefits.

AUTOGENIC TRAINING

This is the business man or woman's de-stressing programme, combining elements of self-hypnosis, yoga and meditation in a no-nonsense scientifically based package. Six simple mental exercises are aimed at inducing profound relaxation: feelings of heaviness (as in 'my right arm is heavy'); warmth ('my left leg is warm'); concentration on the heartbeat; calming the breath; warmth in the stomach; coolness on the forehead.

The course is taught over eight weekly classes, usually at a hospital or private clinic, and once mastered you continue practising on your own.

ALEXANDER TECHNIQUE

This teaches posture improvement so that you stand and move in ways that place less strain on your body. Students report not only feeling in better physical health, but that mental alertness and emotional well-being are enhanced.

Alexander Technique teachers usually work one-to-one. A course consists of 15–30 sessions, after which you should be able to continue on your own.

QI GONG

Pronounced 'chee kung' and translatable as 'energy cultivation', this ancient Chinese system of exercises in posture, breathing and focusing the mind is rapidly gaining popularity in the West. It aims to develop and strengthen your internal energy and control the circulation of the life force, known as 'qi.' There are many variations of qi gong, one of which – and probably best known to Westerners – is **t'ai chi ch'uan,** a graceful series of postures derived from martial arts movements.

PHYSICAL EXERCISE

As described in Chapter Nine, physical activity – walking and gentle exercising – encourages relaxation. In tensing one muscle to create movement, its opposite, or antagonist, muscle has to relax.

CONSTRUCTIVE SELF-TALK

The way in which you perceive a situation will powerfully affect your response. If you're a hostile Type A, you'll imagine everyone is out to get you; if you're someone who believes that nothing you do has any influence (an external locus of control, see page 68), then you'll feel that you have little command of everyday situations.

'Constructive self talk' is a technique to help you reappraise a stressful situation, a kind of encouraging mental monologue which enables you to perceive and respond positively. American psychologists J.C. and J.D. Quick give the following examples (from *Organizational Stress and Preventive Management*, McGraw-Hill 1984):

Situation Driving to work on a day which you know will be full of appointments and potentially stressful meetings

Typical Mental Monologue 'Oh boy, what a day this will be!'
'It's going to be hell.' 'I'll never get it all done.' 'It'll be exhausting.'

Constructive Self-talk Alternative 'This looks like a busy day.' 'The day should be very productive.' 'I'll get a lot accomplished today.' 'I'll earn a good night's rest today.'

Situation Anticipation of a seminar presentation or public address.

Typical Mental Monologue 'What if I blow it?' 'Nobody will laugh at my opening joke.' 'What if they ask about...?' 'I hate talking to groups.'

Constructive Self-talk Alternative 'This ought to be a challenge.' 'I'll take a deep breath and relax.' 'They'll enjoy it.' 'Each presentation goes a bit better.'

Situation Difficulty with a superior at work.

Typical Mental Monologue 'I hate that person.' 'He makes me feel stupid.' 'We'll never get along.'

Constructive Self-talk Alternative 'I don't feel comfortable with him.' 'I let myself get on edge when he's around.' 'It will take some effort to get along.'

THOUGHT-STOPPING

In this technique, another from Quick and Quick, you learn to recognise negative thoughts, attitudes and behaviours – obsessive worrying, for example – and stop them immediately. Visualise a large STOP sign. Then divert your thoughts to something more positive and pleasant. When you're practised at this, you can keep a few agreeable diversionary topics up your sleeve, such as planning a holiday or remembering last weekend's barbecue.

CHAPTER TWELVE

Taking control

How we behave to others – and how we allow them to behave to us – can add to our stress toll. Is your aggressiveness denying other people their rights and making them resentful and unhelpful? Or is your passivity and doormat-ness denying your own rights and letting others walk all over you?

Some people, desperate to be liked by everybody and terrified of confrontations, can't – or won't – ask for help and take on too much because they can't – or won't – say no. Or they are too proud and too easily flattered to refuse. Lorna's boss piles her desk high with assignments that keep her at work late and mean extra hours over the weekend. 'I can't not do it. He says he doesn't trust anybody else to handle it as well,' she says. Fine for Lorna's boss, but her parents haven't seen her for over six months and her husband is so fed up with her devotion to duty that he's seeking the company of a neighbouring divorcee.

Are you aggressive?

Do you:

● react angrily when the situation does not warrant it?
● lean forward, glare, wave your finger at people and raise your voice?
● use phrases like 'if you don't watch out,' 'you must be joking,' 'you should' and 'you ought'?

Are you submissive?

Do you:

● take up the least possible space by hunching your

shoulders, looking at the ground and keeping your arms close to your body?
- speak with an uncertain, whining voice?
- use phrases like 'would you mind very much,' 'it's not terribly important' and tagging 'you know' and 'isn't it?' to the end of your sentences?

Are you assertive?

Do you:
- look people in the eye and stand up straight without slumping and fidgeting?
- speak in a steady voice that doesn't fall or rise at the end of the sentence?
- use phrases like 'I think', 'I want' and 'how do you feel about this?'

BEING ASSERTIVE

Anne Dickson, whose classic book *A Woman In Your Own Right – Assertiveness and You* defines three essential skills.

1 Decide what it is you want or feel and say so – specifically and directly.
2 Stick to your statement, repeating it as many times as is necessary.
3 Deflect any responses that might undermine your position.

For example, when Lorna is asked at the last minute to work late, she could ask herself: Is it really so urgent to finish this tonight? [No, the deadline is tomorrow lunchtime.] What will my boss do if I don't? [He'll sulk but I can live with that. Nobody else puts up with his last minute panics.] What will my husband do if I cancel the cinema? [He's seriously fed up with my extra work and this evening was a real chance to be together.] This reasoning enables her to weigh up her options and make a choice – and when you can choose, you are halfway to being in control. So she replies:

'I know it's important to finish this as soon as possible [acknowledging the urgency], but my husband and I have made arrangements to go to the cinema and I can't do it now [stating her position] but I'll do it first thing in the morning [offering a compromise].'

If her boss persists, she repeats her statement. 'I know you want it done, but I can't stay late this evening. You'll have it in the morning.'

SAYING NO

To say no does not mean you are selfish, mean, rude or aggressive. When somebody asks a favour of you, notice your immediate reaction. If your first response is yes, agree to do it. If it's no, then refuse. And if you can't make up your mind, ask for more information.

When saying no, don't offer too many excuses. By all means explain, as long as you are not doing so because you are anxious or guilty. Depending on your conditioning, you may find it hard to refuse others' requests (women from very traditional backgrounds are particularly susceptible to this). As a result you may take on too many responsibilities, both at work and at home, and then worry because you're too stretched to perform as well as you could.

COMMUNICATING WELL

Good communication is the key to any relationship problem, whether with lovers, friends, customers, colleagues or employers.

Most people are not mindreaders. They will not automatically assume your touchiness or lack of attention at work is due to the fact that your wife is sick or your sitting room ceiling has collapsed. They won't read between the lines – 'ah yes, George thinks that not enough attention has been given to marketing costs' – when all you've said is, 'I'm not very happy about this but let's leave it for the moment'.

The essence of good communication can be summed up in a few simple rules.

- Say what you need to say as clearly and specifically as possible. For example, not just 'I'm unhappy about this' but 'I'm unhappy because I think the costs have not been fully researched'.

- Support this with your non-verbal behaviour. Don't say 'that's okay, no problem' when you're frowning, biting your lip and drumming your fingers.

- Listen to what the other person actually says. This means giving them your full attention and not interrupting. Don't jump to conclusions or put your own interpretation on their words.

- Clarify any areas of doubt by reiterating what you think they said. 'You want me to double-check these figures with the marketing department.'

- Accept other people's opinions and feelings even when they are different from your own.

BUILDING CONFIDENCE

The trick to appearing confident is to act as if you are. People will then listen and respond as if you know what you're talking about, and this will reinforce your own assurance. What was assumed eventually becomes genuine.

Unfair though it may be, remember that first impressions are important. Research by American psychologist Albert Mehrabian revealed that appearance accounts for 55% of what people think about us; our voice for 35%, and what we actually say for a mere 7%.

Tricks will carry us only so far. You need to believe in yourself too. Occupational psychologist Ros Heaton recommends a morning and evening routine of positive affirmations: remind yourself of five things you've achieved today; five things you are good at; five things good about you; five things you like about your appearance; five people who feel warmly about you.

STRESSBREAKERS

- **Maintain eye contact without staring.**
- **Watch your body language. Confident people take up space and don't twitch nervously.**
- **Pause and breathe deeply before speaking. If you hear your voice rising, pull it down at the end of the sentence.**
- **Be prepared. Know your facts before going into a meeting, make notes for a speech.**
- **Choose clothes that fit and are appropriate, so that you're not fretting about your appearance.**
- **Dress for the job you want, not the one you have.**

MAKING TIME

If you manage your time more efficiently not only will your stress levels be reduced, but you will:
- be more productive
- enjoy your work more
- have more time for leisure

● be able to plan ahead instead of struggling to keep up
● be more creative because you will have time to think.

You could have problems with time management if you answer yes to the following questions.

1 Do you often have feelings of panic when you think of how much you have to do?

2 Do you frequently find yourself trying to attend to several jobs at the same time?

3 Do you often have to stay late or take routine work home in order to finish it?

4 When you've been away on work-related assignments, do you find your desk piled high on your return?

5 Do you sometimes wake up at night remembering things you should have done during the day?

6 Do you frequently find yourself putting off jobs until 'later?'

7 Are you easily distracted from the task in hand?

8 Do you often have difficulty getting started on a new task or on the day's work?

9 Do you sometimes find notes or names or numbers in your own handwriting without remembering what they are about?

10 Are you rather slow in making decisions?

11 Do you pride yourself on always being busy?

12 Do you spend time on minor details, in spite of the fact that many tasks obey the law of diminishing returns?

13 Do you frequently lose time fuming or fretting after clashes with difficult colleagues or clients?

14 Are you often engaged in tasks that could be done by people without your qualifications or training?

> **15 When you brief others, do they frequently need to come back for clarification or further information?**
>
> **16 Do you have difficulty terminating interviews or conversations once you have obtained the information you need?**
>
> **(taken from *Managing Time* by David Fontana, British Books 1993).**

Being assertive and saying no are part of time management skills. So is the ability to prioritise, or to decide what is important. An American psychologist who studied top performers in all walks of life discovered certain characteristics in common. They weren't workaholics who had lost control of their time. They were motivated and energised by goals which they set themselves. Holidays weren't skimped because they couldn't afford to be away, but used for rest and creative thinking. They didn't try to be perfect. And they delegated any tasks that could be done by other people.

Many books have been written on time management. Some of them are very good indeed, but only worth taking the time to read if you are prepared to put their advice into practice.

Basic rules found in most are:

1 Set aside a period of planning for the week ahead. Check that appointments don't clash and allocate time for particular tasks.

2 Ask yourself whether you need to do a particular job yourself or whether it can be passed on to someone else.

3 Every day allow for ten minutes' planning time, either by yourself or with core staff. (One trick is to hold quick meetings standing up).

4 Make a daily 'To Do' list. You can have an A list and a B list, or urgent, not so urgent and when there is time lists. However

structured, mark those items which must be done today and those which can wait, and tick off each item as it's completed.

5 Allow only a certain time for routine chores.

6 Make yourself unavailable if there is something that must be finished and you can't afford interruptions. Shut the door, put the telephone answering machine on. If you are interrupted, tell the caller you will ring back in a specified time – and do so.

7 There are only so many hours in the day and some time must be made for relaxation, even if you have to mark it in your weekly schedule. You should never be too busy to relax for an hour every evening before bed; to have an hour a day for a hobby or interest; to exercise for half an hour at least four times a week; and to take two and a half uninterrupted hours a day for meals. Even if eight hours are spent in bed, this still leaves 11 hours a day for work (less travelling time) which is surely enough for anybody.

Delegation is particularly difficult for anyone haunted by an often deeply ingrained insecurity who can't bear to risk losing control. Every facet of their job must be monitored. It can also be genuinely difficult to decide which tasks to delegate. Some worth considering are:

● fact finding studies
● first drafts of written material
● problem analyses and possible solutions
● routine tasks
● feasibility studies
● progress reports
● follow-up tasks

Remember to give a clear brief about the job; guidelines on when to refer back to you; opportunities to use initiative (an incentive for juniors to show their stuff!); and praise for a job well done.

CHAPTER THIRTEEN

With a little help

A number of therapeutic techniques are found increasingly valuable when coping with stress. It may cost a little money – practitioners can be hard to find on the NHS – but in pre-empting burnout and affording you time to relax, it could be a worthwhile investment.

NON-CONVENTIONAL THERAPIES

Many fall into what is called complementary or non-conventional therapy, which has always understood the importance of treating the whole person. As the new science of psychoneuroimmunology is discovering, mind and body are inextricably bound together, the health of one affecting that of the other. The effects of stress demonstrate this very well; mental states of tension and anxiety manifest in physical conditions such as headaches, irritable bowel syndrome and heart disease. Conversely, treating the body may soothe the mind.

If you consult a non-conventional practitioner, do make sure he or she is adequately trained and reputable. Ask if they belong to a recognised organisation and be prepared to check it out. Avoid any practitioner who claims miracle cures or suggests you abandon conventional medicine. It is always advisable to inform your doctor if you are considering non-conventional therapy; in fact, you may even find that he or she can recommend a practitioner.

Acupuncture

According to traditional Chinese medicine, the universal life energy known as qi is concentrated in our bodies in invisible channels beneath the skin called meridians. By inserting needles into specific points along these meridians, acupuncturists aim to restore the flow of qi when its balance has been disturbed, due to disease, poor diet and emotional disorder.

Acupuncture needles are of fine stainless steel and insertion is quick and usually painless. Sessions usually last from 30 to 90 minutes, once or twice a week, and some improvement should be expected after five sessions.

Aromatherapy

Aromatic essences and essential oils, extracted from wild or cultivated plants, are claimed to have healing properties when these are added to a carrier oil and massaged into the skin, inhaled, or used in a bath. The oils have different effects – those most frequently recommended for stress include cedarwood, camomile, clary sage, geranium, juniper, lavender, marjoram and tangerine.

A full-body massage by a qualified aromatherapist is an intensely relaxing experience, especially for anyone who is so stressed they have difficulty in calming themselves down.

Alternatively, a few drops of oil added to the bath at night can be a very soothing way to unwind.

Some precautions: Never use an undiluted oil directly on the skin, unless specifically indicated, nor swallow them. Avoid contact with the eyes. Keep oils out of reach of children and if you are pregnant, consult a qualified aromatherapist as some oils can be harmful in pregnancy.

Biofeedback

When wired to an electromyograph, a machine that translates electrical impulses in the muscles into signals that can be seen on a screen or heard as a tone, people learn to recognise the onset of tension and use relaxation skills to defuse it. Similarly when changes of brainwave patterns are recorded on an electroencephalograph, people can be taught to shift into the alpha wave length that is associated with the relaxed awareness achieved by meditation.

Massage

Kneading and stroking the body's soft tissues (skin and muscles) with varying degrees of pressure brings a therapeutic feeling of relaxation and comfort. Stroking gives a constant pressure and relaxes the muscles; movements that knead or use friction improve circulation. It can stimulate the nervous system and the waste drainage (lymphatic) systems. The sense of invigoration and well-being that results can help prevent disease by dispelling the stress hormones that weaken the immune system.

It's possible to give yourself a limited massage, but far more satisfying to find a qualified massage therapist.

STRESSBREAKERS

- Massage the fingers of each hand in turn (take one slow breath for each finger and thumb). Concentrate on how soft it feels. Do this five times a day.
- With the fingertips of each hand, give your scalp a vigorous shampoo rub, focussing on the hairline.
- Place the fingers of both hands on either side of the back of your neck. Breathing deeply, press and move them slowly outwards from the centre.

> ● **Arms straight, clasp your hands one inside the other, fingers unlocked, behind your back. Hunch both shoulders forward, hold for 30 seconds, then relax. Still clasping your hands, try to get your elbows as close together as possible behind your back. Hold for 30 seconds and relax.**

Osteopathy

Osteopaths believe that a badly aligned spine can cause muscle and nerve problems in other parts of the body and these in turn contribute to the individual's perception of stress.

For instance, it's not uncommon for women who suffer premenstrual syndrome to book an osteopathy session when they know it will coincide with a heavy work schedule.

When there is less strain on the muscles and joints, all the body's systems function smoothly. Osteopaths work with their hands, diagnosing and treating problem areas by manipulating and stretching soft tissues and mobilising joints.

Reflexology

This is based on the theory that areas known as reflex points on the feet, hands and face correspond to each organ of the body. It's believed that these points are joined by channels of energy. By applying specific pressure to the points, a practitioner can release blocked energy and restore balance to the body's functions.

Shiatsu

Like acupuncture, shiatsu (Japanese for 'finger pressure') works on key points in energy pathways known as meridians. It's a combination of massage, pressure and components of physiotherapy and chiropractic. Instead of using needles, the practitioner employs fingers, thumbs, elbows, knees and even feet to exert pressure, as well as rotating the limbs and stretching the back. The aim is to disperse pent-up energy (jitsu) or conserve it where needed (kyo). Unlike therapeutic massage where you are expected to undress, you remain fully clothed throughout treatment.

PSYCHOLOGICAL SUPPORT

Dealing with depression (see page 17)

Sometimes all the massage, self-help and support of friends is not enough to stop the downward spiral. When tired and under pressure, we can all feel 'down', and usually a good night's sleep or a break from work is enough to revive us. But sometimes your genetic inheritance, your personality, life experiences and stress factors come together to nudge you into real depression. When this happens, you are strongly advised to consult your GP; there are a number of extraordinary new approaches to deal with all kinds of depression.

Counselling is usually the first step and often sufficient in itself to pull you out of a slough of despondency. But sometimes stronger measures are needed. The new breed of antidepressants (known as selective 5-HT re-uptake inhibitors), which include the so-called wonder drug Prozac, have fewer side-effects than tricyclic antidepressants, are non-addictive and harder to overdose on. In many cases, they have been remarkably successful, especially when combined with psychotherapy.

Talking it through

Talking through problems with a psychologist or counsellor is thankfully no longer seen as a sign of weakness or insanity, but a sensible and effectual means of coping, especially when the traditional emotional props – priests, family doctors, wise old relatives and neighbours – are in short supply.

This is especially true if stress symptoms such as anxiety, pessimism, irrational reactions to colleagues, panic attacks, obsessions and compulsions are interfering with your work and personal relationships. Counselling and psychotherapy are available free on the NHS, so consult your GP first, but some areas of the country are better served than others. Your workplace may have a confidential counselling scheme or run stress management groups; or you may prefer to seek help privately.

There are a number of different professions involved in this field, and it's helpful to know what they do.

Psychiatrists are doctors who specialise in mental problems and tend to treat patients primarily with drugs.

Psychologists have taken a university degree and specialise in a number of areas. Clinical psychologists deal with emotional and behavioural problems and use a variety of methods, usually behavioural and cognitive therapy.

Psychoanalysts explore the relationship between the conscious and unconscious mind, usually by examining childhood experiences and relationships – the so-called 'talking cure'.

Psychotherapists also help you examine past experiences and relationships in order to bring about changes in your thinking and behaviour. Treatment tends to be long-term; six months would be the minimum, and two years the norm.

Counsellors tend to focus on a particular problem and the treatment tends to be more overtly supportive and shorter –

weeks not months or years.

Psychotherapists and therapists employ a number of therapies to help people deal with stress, both the symptoms and reasons for them. A short-term therapy that is proving very helpful for stress-related conditions – especially those negative thinkers who tend to describe a glass as half empty rather than half full – is **cognitive behavioural therapy**. This helps people see things differently and discover hidden sources of strength that enable them to solve their own problems. Previous experiences condition us to think about ourselves in a particular way, which in turn affects our attitudes and emotions and the way we deal with situations. By changing your thinking to be more positive, you change your behaviour. Your anxiety may not go away – it could take years of psychoanalysis to uncover *why* you are anxious – but it can be managed. Eventually, as positive experiences increasingly overlay the negative ones, you acquire more confidence in your coping abilities.

HOW TO FIND THE RIGHT COUNSELLOR FOR YOU

Try to be clear about what kind of therapy you seek as each has its particular approach. Do you want it to be friendly and supportive ('warm') or analytic and detached ('cool')? Do you want to work on your feelings or your thinking or behaviour? Would you prefer the practitioner to be in charge or do you like to be in control? Do you feel more comfortable in an equal relationship, or working in a group of people rather than one-to-one?

Many practitioners will agree to an initial free consultation – they are also deciding whether they can help *you*. Don't hesitate to ask questions; you will be revealing some of your innermost thoughts and feelings to this person.

- What qualifications does the practitioner have and what was the training?
- How many years has the practitioner been practising?
- Is the practitioner a member of a professional organisation? (Check with the British Association for Counselling or the United Kingdom Council for Psychotherapy (UKCP).)
- Does he or she receive regular supervision from another qualified practitioner?
- What is the practitioner's approach? What can you expect to happen during the sessions?
- How long is the course of therapy likely to last?
- Will there be regular reviews of the way it's progressing?

If you have any doubts at all, or if at any time you feel uneasy about what is suggested, then discuss it. Remember that you can always choose to stop the therapy.

CHAPTER FOURTEEN

Making progress

Check your progress in learning to cope with stressful situations. Keeping a Stress Diary for a month or two helps you record difficult situations and monitor your responses.

Every day, note any stressful incidents and the people involved. How did you react? What were your thoughts and what did you actually do? What, on reflection, should you have done? Are there any common threads?

For example, you might recognise that it is mostly when speaking to strangers, either in meetings or on the telephone, that you stammer, gabble or jumble your words. What can you do about this? You could:

- take a deep breath and relax just before speaking
- speak slowly and deliberately
- investigate speech therapy.

HOW WELL ARE YOU DOING?

Do you:
- always eat breakfast?
- have at least one balanced meal a day?
- drink less than three cups of caffeine (tea,
- coffee or cola) a day?
- drink one litre of water a day?
- eat a variety of fruit and vegetables a day?
- keep within the appropriate weight for your height?
- limit your alcohol intake to 21 units (if male) or 14 units (if female) spread over the week?

- not smoke?
- exercise so that you are warm and out of breath for a total of 30 minutes on most days of the week?
- manage seven hours' sleep at least four nights a week?
- have enough money for your needs?
- watch your posture when standing, sitting and driving?
- ensure your chair and desk are at a comfortable height?
- monitor your body for tension?
- have a means of physical and mental relaxation?
- know when and how to consult your doctor or therapist?
- give and receive affection frequently?
- have a relative within 50 miles on whom you can rely?
- have a network of friends and acquaintances?
- regularly enjoy a social evening?
- have a close friend to confide in?
- express feelings of anger or anxiety?
- think positively?
- laugh easily?
- listen to what people are saying?
- try to see the other person's point of view?
- discuss any emotional/sexual problems with your partner?
- have a quiet time to yourself every day?
- do something for fun at least once a week?
- take strength from philosophical, religious or other deeply held beliefs?

Scoring. Score one point for yes/always; two points for probably/usually; three points for sometimes; four points for rarely/not; five points for no/never. If your score is less than 75, you're doing well. The higher your score – the more vulnerable you still are to stress.

WHAT TO DO

Look at other ways of coping that the quiz questions might suggest. For example, if you realise that your day is so crammed that you have no time to yourself, give yourself permission to close the door and rest, read a novel or play the Benny Goodman CD that nobody else in the family can stand.

Allowing ourselves enjoyment is sometimes half the battle; if you're still doubtful, remember that those close to you will function better if you are relaxed and good-humoured.

Stress management courses can be very helpful and will put you in touch with other people in a similar situation.For further information contact Health at Work at the HEA Business Unit or Relaxation for Living. (See Resources for addresses.)

Resources

FURTHER READING

Edware A. Charlesworth and Ronald G. Nathan, *Stress Management* (Ballantine Books 1993)

Cary L. Cooper, Rachel D. Cooper and Lynn H. Eaker *Living With Stress* (Penguin 1988)

Stephen R. Covey, *The 7 Habits of Highly Effective People,* (Simon & Schuster 1989)

Marilyn Davidson and Cary Cooper, *Stress and the Woman Manager* (Martin Robertson 1983)

Philippa Davies, *Personal Power* (Piatkus 1992)

Philippa Davies, *Total Confidence* (Piatkus 1994)

Anne Dickson, *A Woman In Your Own Right* (Quartet Books 1982)

Robert S. Eliot, *From Stress to Strength: How to Lighten Your Load and Save Your Life* (Bantam 1994)

Helen Froggatt and Paul Stamp, *Managing Pressure At Work* (BBC Books 1991)

David Fontana, *Managing Time* (The British Psychological Society BPS Books 1993)

Peter Hanson, *Stress for Success* (Pan 1990)

Peter Hanson, *The Joy of Stress* (Pan 1988)

Clare Maxwell Hudson, *The Complete Book of Massage* (Dorling Kindersley 1988)

Jon Kabat-Zinn, *Full Catastrophe Living* (Delta 1990)

Alix Kirsta, *The Book of Stress Survival* (Thorsons 1991)

Lindsay Knight, *Talking to a Stranger,* (Fontana 1986)

Sarah Litvinoff, *The Relate Guide to Better Relationships* (Ebury Press 1991)

Sarah Litvinoff and Lucy Daniels (eds), *Balancing Work and Home* (A Parents At Work Publication 1994)

John Nicholson, *How Do You Manage?*, (BBC Books 1992)

Dr. Chandra Patel, *Understanding Stress*, (Which? Books and Hodder & Stoughton 1992)

J.C. and J.D. Quick *Organizational Stress and Preventive Management* (McGraw-Hill 1984)

Margaret Sills and Ann Aris, *Positive Stress At Work* (HEA 1994)

Jenny Sutcliffe, *The Complete Book of Relaxation Techniques* (Headline 1991)

Murray Watts and Professor Cary. L. Cooper, *Relax – Dealing With Stress* (BBC Books 1992)

Redford Williams and Virginia Williams, *Anger Kills* (Times Books, Random House 1993)

Georgia Witkin-Lanoil, *Coping With Stress – A Woman's Guide* (Sheldon 1990)

Anne Woodham, *Get Up And Go!* (Headline 1994)

Anne Woodham, *HEA Guide to Complementary Medicine and Therapies*, (Health Education Authority 1994)

USEFUL ADDRESSES

Alcoholics Anonymous, P.O. Box 1, Stonebow House, Stonebow, York YO1 2NJ (01904 644026/7/8/9) (24 hour telephone service 0171 352 3001)

Action on Smoking and Health (ASH), 109 Gloucester Place, London W1H 4EJ (0171 935 3519)

Aromatherapy Organisations Council, 3 Latymer Close, Braybrooke, Market Harborough, Leicester LE16 8LN (018588 434242)

Association of Reflexologists, 25 Friars Walk, Lewes BN7 2LF (01273 479020)

Biofeedback, Maxwell Cade Foundation, 9 Chatsworth Road, London NW2 4BJ (0181 451 0083)

British Association for Autogenic Training and Therapy, 18 Holtsmere Close, Garston, Watford, Herts WD2 6NG

British Association for Counselling, 1 Regent Place, Rugby, Warwickshire CV21 2PJ (01788 578328)

British Complementary Medicine Association, St. Charles Hospital, Exmoor Street, London W10 6DZ (0181 964 1205)

British Massage Therapy Council, Greenbank House, 65a Adelphi Street, Preston, PR1 7BH. (01772 881 063)

The British Reflexology Association, Monks Orchard, Whitbourne, Worcester WR6 5RB (01886 21207)

British Wheel of Yoga, 1 Hamilton Place, Boston Road, Sleaford, Lincolnshire NG34 7ES (01529 306851)

Clare Maxwell-Hudson School of Massage, P.O. Box 457, London NW2 4BR

Council for Acupuncture, 179 Gloucester Place, London NW1 6DX (0171 724 5756)

Depressives Anonymous, 36 Chestnut Avenue, Beverley, Humberside HU17 9QU (01482 860619)

Health At Work, HEA Business Unit, 64 Burgate, Canterbury, Kent CT1 2HJ

Migraine Trust, 45 Great Ormond Street, London WC1N 3HD (0171 278 2676)

MIND, National Association for Mental Health, Head Office: Granta House, Broadway, London E15 4BQ (0181 519 2122)

National Association for Premenstrual Syndrome, P.O. Box 72, Sevenoaks, Kent TN13 1XQ (0732 741 709)

Osteopathic Information Service, P.O. Box 2074, Reading, Berkshire RG1 4SQ (01734 576585/566260)

Parents at Work (formerly The Working Mothers Association), 77 Holloway Road, London N7 8JZ (0171 700 5771)

Phobics' Society, 4 Cheltenham Road, Chorlton cum Hardy, Manchester M21 9QN (0161 881 1937)

United Kingdom Council for Psychotherapy (UKCP), Regent's College, Inner Circle, Regent's Park, London NW1 4NS (0171 487 7554)

The Redcliffe Project (The Chemical Dependency Centre), 11 Redcliffe Gardens, London SW10 9BG (0171 352 2552)

Relate National Marriage Guidance, Herbert Gray College, Little Church Street, Rugby CV21 3AP (01788 573241) (see telephone book for local branches)

Relaxation for Living Trust, 168-170 Oatlands Drive, Weybridge, Surrey KT13 9ET (01932 831000)

Revital Health Shop, 3A The Colonnades, 123 - 151 Buckingham Palace Road, London SW1. For mail order of Melaton:- telephone 0800 252875

Samaritans (see telephone book for local branches)

School of T'ai-chi Ch'uan, 5 Tavistock Place, London WC1H 9SN (0181 444 6445)

The Shiatsu Society, 5 Foxcote, Wokingham, Berks RTG11 3PG (01734 730836)

Society of Teachers of the Alexander Technique, 20 London House, 266 Fulham Road, London SW10 9EL (0171 351 0828)

Yoga for Health Foundation, Ickwell Bury, Biggleswade, Bedfordshire SG18 9EF (01767 627271)